Toxteth Tales

KEN HAYTER

Looking at Liverpool ONE from Victoria
Monument after the blitz of 1941

The War Years

First published in 2017
by Palatine Books,
Carnegie House,
Chatsworth Road
Lancaster LA1 4SL
www.palatinebooks.com

British Library Cataloguing-in-Publication data
A catalogue record for this book is available from the British Library

ISBN 13: 978-1-910837-13-9

Designed and typeset by Carnegie Book Production
www.carnegiepublishing.co.uk

Printed and bound by Ashford Colour Press

Contents

The 1940s and '50s

'Liverpool: a city where everybody
seemed to know everybody else,
where nobody seemed to have any
money, but everyone seemed happy.
A city of safe and cosy little streets
of 'two-up, two-downs' where two
or three generations of families lived
within a few doors of each other and
often behind one door.'

Preamble

'What with our streets and the bombed sites, the shops and parks,
the swimming baths on Lodgy, the picture houses, and
the City itself, we lived in a paradise for children.'

I am fond of children, except boys.

(*The Letters*, LEWIS CARROLL)

WHEN I WAS A CHILD, I was a Scouser.

But then I moved away from the Liverpool 8 of my childhood, to be left with only memories. It is these memories that are the basis of the anecdotes that follow.

I was a child in the years during and just after the last world war, when hundreds of tiny communities, called streets, were the lifeblood of the City of Liverpool, and the Port, its heart.

Lodge Lane, Liverpool 8

Liverpool: a city where everybody seemed to know everybody else, where nobody seemed to have any money, but everyone seemed to be happy. A city of safe and cosy little streets of 'two-up, two-downs' where two or three generations of families lived within a few doors of each other and often behind one door.

It was a time when many of the men were in the armed forces, away from home, and when our mothers' lives seemed an endless round of washing clothes, shopping on Lodge Lane, cooking, cleaning the doorstep with 'donkeystone', then washing the pavement down to the cobbled road-way. They were always at work, except for when they gathered on doorsteps to gossip, to talk about anyone who wasn't with them; about who was getting more from the butcher than their ration book allowed, and what they were probably doing to get it. All of them talking, and none of them listening.

But for a child, life was an endless round of playing out.

We played in dusty streets just the right size for 'Kick-the-Can', most with an air-raid shelter purpose built for 'King of the Castle'; with the horse-drawn bin-lorry a once a week joyride and a source of nourishment for Grandad's allotment.

Liver Building

2

When we reached the age of five, we went to school. There, our teachers tried to convince us that the exploits of Janet and John were more important than the adventures of Dick Barton, Special Agent. When that failed, they tried teaching us to add three pretend apples to another two, as a substitute for stealing a real one from the barrel outside the Cash and Carry on Lodgy.

We humoured them, waiting for the bell to sound playtime, when we would erupt through our classroom doors into the playground, to hang onto the schoolyard railings shouting minor obscenities at passers-by, or exhorting women shoppers: 'Ey, Missus, buy us a penny balm-cake from Williams', go on. I'll give you the money later, honest!'

I suppose most people looking back to their childhood remember only the happy times, and I am no different; though I would add carefree to happy, when trying to explain how the 1940s and early '50s might be a little different from today's childhood experience. They certainly seemed to be happy, carefree days spent in a paradise for children. A paradise of six-penny matinees at the Tunnel Road Picturedrome, if Grandad managed a couple of days' work on the Docks and added his thri'pence to my 'thri'penny joey' pocket money; or an even cheaper four-penny matinee at the Playhouse on Smithdown Road, if Grandad wasn't chosen that week. Of 'penny returns' on the 5W tram to the countryside of Woolton, or much rarer Tu-penny return ferry trips across the river, to the seaside and fairground at New Brighton.

Not that you needed pocket money. There were always the weekend adventures in Sefton and Prince's Park, and the endless games on the streets and on the bombed sites that littered our city.

Is it a failing memory? Were we really always happy?

Perhaps not all of the time, but I think we must have been, at least for most of the time; but then I was only a child.

If the grown-ups were not so happy, they didn't tell the children.

Maybe my mother sometimes worried about where tomorrow's dinner was coming from. If she did, she did not tell me; but gave me a sugar butty instead of dinner, 'For bein' a good boy,' even if the evidence said otherwise.

If air-raid sirens and the grumbling of German bomber engines frightened them, they said nothing, except to hurry us to the concrete shelter with their arms around us, protecting us from horrors never discussed in the presence of a child. There, in dank gloom, we sprawled on sacking covered bunks to play 'I spy with my little eye' until the 'All clear' signalled our safe return to another day. And in the early morning sky of that new day, we might see smoke and dust rising from where someone's house had stood, before the sirens sounded. Our mothers would hurry us indoors, whilst they stood on the doorstep staring at the dust cloud, wondering who it was that might not see the new day.

Tagus Street, like all of its neighbours, was so narrow that a hop, skip and a jump across its tarred cobbles took you from one side to the other, whilst a short run along the granite-edged pavement took you to the longer and wider shopping thoroughfare of Lodge Lane.

'Lodgy' was one of many long roads of shops that led eventually to the dual carriageways radiating from the city centre, with tramcars rattling along their own middle lane. A 'Penny-return' on any tram from anywhere, took you to the Docks and back to anywhere.

Like many others, Tagus Street suffered from the attention of Hitler's Luftwaffe when his aircraft couldn't find the docks, but dropped their bombs anyway; but my family and our neighbours were lucky. All but the very bottom of our street remained intact, and the bit that was destroyed was our nearest playground, our very own bombed site, our 'debbie'. But whispered conversations amongst gossiping women in the mid war years, hinted of streets and homes not so lucky; of friends they had lost and of children who would never play out again. But our mothers did not tell us, and we played our games on the tragedy of others.

Many of our dads were away in the forces and had been for years: so long in a child's life that some of us were not sure what a dad was. It didn't seem to matter much, because our mothers did all the loving we wanted and more than we needed.

Times were hard, they say; and so I'm sure they were, for our mams and dads, but not for us. They didn't tell the children that times were hard and we were not old enough to recognise the strain on their faces behind the smiles, and so we were carefree.

We were probably poor, but we never knew it: we seemed to be just like everyone else. Some might say we were deprived; but deprived of what?

If we were, nobody told the children and so in our ignorance we just had to be happy and contented in our dusty streets. In any case, we were far too busy to listen. There were games to be played in summers when it was always sunny: when the all-pervasive dust from the bombed sites made the air a cosy haze. And yet more games in the winter months when it always snowed: when smoke from a thousand coal-fires added a sooty coat to the crisp whiteness of the snow.

Ours was a comfy safe world of mams, grandads, grandmas, a few aunts and uncles, and lots of children. A constant world occasionally interrupted by a visit from someone on leave from the war, someone called Dad.

What with our streets and the bombed sites, the shops and parks, the swimming baths on Lodgy, the picture houses, and the City itself, we lived in a paradise for children.

But as we grew older, someone told us we were not happy, that our streets were slums, that we were deprived. And we believed them. And so our childhood paradise was lost: lost as childhood gave way to the years, 'Kick the Can' to work and Tagus Street to the demolition experts. And we left our childhood homes to seek the semi-detachments of new estates.

The tales that follow are written as stories in an attempt to recapture the atmosphere of a childhood in Liverpool 8, in the years during and just after the war. 'Tagus Street, Family and Friends', the first chapter, sets the scene for the stories by introducing some of the characters and their little bit of Liverpool 8.

All of the events in the tales are as true as my memory allows and, whilst the characters are fictional, they can be seen as real in the sense that they are synthesised from recollections of all of the members of my family, my friends and our neighbours. It would be nice to think that the 'real' people would see something of themselves in one or other of the characters; indeed, I would be disappointed if they did not. However, if they do, I must

DURNING ROAD TRAGEDY

'whispered conversations amongst gossiping women in the mid war years, hinted at streets and homes not so lucky, of friends they had lost and of children who would never play out again'

5

disclaim all responsibility for arousing their suspicions, except that is, for the character named 'Charlie'.

I would be disappointed if 'Charlie', my brother in the stories, was not instantly recognised by Charlie, my brother; even though it is possible that, because of the frailty of my memory, some of the events involving 'Charlie' may in fact have had nothing to do with him. The words and actions of the character in the stories are, however, entirely in keeping with the real Charlie, though I expect him to deny that there is even the slightest resemblance between them.

Charlie apart, I do take responsibility for including one real person. That person is me: Kenneth Hayter, with my name translated by the poetry of Scouse, from Hayter to Potater to Potato to Spud.

A Scouse thesaurus

A common experience of visitors to the 'Pool' is to find themselves engaged in conversation over a pint in one of our pubs with a few of the locals. The trouble is that they often haven't the faintest idea of what we are talking about. This Thesaurus is intended for our visitors, in the hope that it will make their visit more enjoyable ... and keep them out of trouble!

Included are a number of linked words where each word in the link might have its own meaning or, perhaps, no meaning at all; but together they form a common Scouse expression.

SCOUSE   QUEEN'S ENGLISH

A   I (as in 'A don't know what to do': 'I don't know what to do')

Aggro   Aggravation, antagonism

Airyated   Excited

Ang on   Wait a moment

Ang one on   Hit, strike

Antwacky   Old, out of date

Anyroad   In any case

Ard-arse   Cold personality, not emotional

Ardclock   Cheeky, impudent

Ardfaced   Cheeky, impudent

Arrers   Darts

Arr-ey!   A plea (as in 'Arr-ey! Don't do that': 'Please desist')

Arr kid   My sister, my brother

Ax   Ask

Back-crack   Jigger (see below)

Bags   Staking claim (as in 'I bags that sweet!')

Barley   I give in, so please desist (sometimes prefixed 'I bags' to add emphasis of complete capitulation)

Barmy   Not very bright, insane

Barny   Argument

Batter   Hit, strike, thump, marmalise (as in 'I'll batter you, you little get')

Beetlecrushers   Boots

Belt   Hit, strike

Berrer   Better

Bevvy   Drink (of beer)

Biddy   Elderly lady, head louse

Bin   Been

Binnie   Binman, refuse collector

Blind   Used to emphasise something (as in ''E won't take a blind bit-a notice': 'He will not take any notice')

Blind Scouse   A mutton based stew, with no mutton

Buggeroff   Please go away

Bumstarver   Short jacket

Butty   Slice of bread, sandwich

Cack-anded   Clumsy

Carn   Can't

Casey   Football (leather, with lace to seal opening for inserting blow-up bladder – pre: kissing football legends)

Cazzie   Shore of River Mersey near Aigburth Vale

Chocker   Full (up) (as in 'Ye won't get served in der la, it's chocker')

Ciggy   Cigarette

Clat tale tit   Informer

Clock   Face (a person's, not a clock's); See (as in 'I clocked 'im wiv another judy': 'I saw him with another woman')

Clubman   Insurance or debt collector

Cob-on   Bad mood

Cogger   Of the Catholic faith

Cooey   Jigger (see below), a call for attention

Cop shop   Police station

Corpy   House belonging to local authority

Coupler   Two, couple of

Cozzie   Swimming costume

Crack on   Acknowledge (as in "E won't crack on': 'He is ignoring me')

Cudden   Couldn't

Dale   They will

Dancers   Stairs

Darrell   That will

Dat   That

De   The

Dead   To emphasize something (as in 'Dey are a dead spit': 'They are very alike')

Debbie   Debris, bombed site

Dee   The

Decko   Look at

Deffo   Definitely, surely

De gear   Excellent

Dem   Them

Desert-wellies   Sandals

Divvy, divwoll   Idiot

Dockers umbrella   Overhead railway

Donkeystone   Light-yellow stone for cleaning doorsteps

Douse   Look out (as in 'You keep douse for a scuffer': 'You keep a lookout for a policeman')

Ello dur   Hello

Entry   Jigger (see below)

Ey-la   Hello there, my good fellow

Eye wiped   Get it wrong (as in "E tried to gerrof wid dis judy, but 'e gorris eye wiped – she told 'im to buggeroff')

Fades   Over ripe fruit (usually apples)

Farder Bunloaf   Priest

Feller   Boyfriend, husband

Fine pair-a knockers   Lovely figure (of a lady)

Firebobby   Fireman

Flicks   Films, cinema

Gammy 'anded   Left handed

Gawpin   Looking

Ge   Get

Gis   Give (as in 'Gis a bit': 'Please may I have some')

Gob   Mouth

Gob on   Not very happy (as in "E's gorra gob on, 'is judy's left 'im.')

Gobshite   Someone you don't like

Go-ed   Please proceed

Good skin   Nice person

Gorran   Got a, has a (as in "E's gorran ead as big as Berknead

(Birkenhead)': 'He's a little pompous')

Gorrup   Arose, dressed (as in "E's gorrup like a pox-doctor's clerk': 'He is well dressed')

Gozzie   Cross-eyed

Gunner   Going to

Im   Him, husband

Ir   It (as in 'Giv ir'ere': 'Give it to me')

I'yer   Hello

Jigger   Footpath (between the yards of back-to-back houses, running the whole length of a street, or dissecting rows of houses: usually half way along a street)

Joey   Three-penny coin (sometimes thri'penny joey)

Jowler   Jigger (see above)

Judy   Girl, girlfriend, wife

Kecks   Trousers

Kilt   Killed

La   You, Sir (as in 'Y'all right la?': Are you all right, Sir?')

Lady Muck   Woman with airs and graces

Lanny   Landing stage (for ferries)

Lecky   Electricity

Left footer   Of the Catholic faith

Lemmy   Let me

Loosie   'Loose' cigarette (a cigarette bought singly)

Lord Muck   Man with airs and graces

Lugole   Ear

Mam   Mother

Mardy   Sulky

Marmalise   (see Batter)

Marrer   Matter

Me   My

Mickey Drippin   Pseudonym

Millyins   Quite a few, quite expensive (as in 'It cost millyins')

Minesweeper   Eater/drinker of any left over food/beer

Mingy   Mean

Mitts   Hands

Mizzle   Disappear

Muck-in   Take/eat as much as you like (as in 'Muck in, yer at your Grannie's')

Mug   Treat (as in 'I'll mug yer to a bevvy.')

Of   Have (as in 'I could of done that': 'I could have done that')

Ollies   Marbles

Oo Flung Dung   Any Chinese person

One-a Lewis's   Poser

Ower   Our

Owl   Old

Owl feller   Husband

Owl gurl   Wife

Parish   National Assistance, benefits

Parlitic   Paralytic, drunk

Plenny   Plenty

Pool   Liverpool (usually 'De Pool')

Proddy Dog   Protestant

Rantan   Knock on door (persistently)

Ropey   Not very good

Sag   Play truant
Saggin   Playing truant
Sarnie   Sandwich
Savvy   This afternoon
Scarper   Run away
Scouse   Liverpool dialect, mutton based stew (from 'Lobscouse')
Scouser   Liverpudlian
Scuffer   Policeman
Skewl   School
Spec   Place (as in 'This is a good spec to see the goal from')
Starved   Very cold
Sterry   Sterilised milk

Ta   Thank you (as in 'Ta la': 'Thank you sir.')
Tally   Together, but not married (as in ''E's livin' tally wiv 'is judy')
Tallyman   Debt collector
Tarrar   Goodbye
Tarrar-well   Goodbye
Tatty   Less than perfect
Tatty-ead   Affectionate greeting (as in ''Ello tatty-ead.'), Disparaging description of someone.
Tick   Loan (as in 'Purrit on tick': 'I'll pay for it later')
Tilly Mint   Pseudonym
Tingy (Hard 'g')   Person whose name is unknown
Tizzy   Excited, confused
Tod   Alone
T'morrer   Tomorrow
T'rar   Goodbye
Trollop   Unsavoury woman, woman of ill repute

Under dee arm   Not very good, not very well (as in 'I'm under dee arm, doc': 'I'm not very well, doctor')
Urdo   Coiffure
Us   I, me

Wack   You (as in 'I'yer wack': 'Hello there, you')
Wacker   Liverpudlian
Wanner   Want to
Wellie   Wellington boot, hit, thump, etc.
Wurld   World

Ye-what?   What did you say?
Yew   You (singular)
Yews   You (singular or plural)
Yiss   Yes
Yisstiddy   Yesterday
Y'know like   Detailed explanation (as in 'Yer can't travel faster than light, y'know like': Full explanation of Einstein's Theory of Relativity)
Yokker   Spit

To conclude the Thesaurus, I thought it might be an idea to include a few sentences and composite words in the Scouse language. This might give the reader a better sense of our dialect, or otherwise convince them that there is no sense at all to it.

'Ail Marey, muvver of God!: I am surprised!

Carn 'ear a blind word 'e sais: I cannot hear him.

Dey play tick wiv atchets: Not a very nice neighbourhood.

'E cudden stop a pig in a jigger: He is bowlegged.

'Ere's y'rat, what's yer 'urry?: You are very welcome to stay, but it is getting rather late.

'E's gawpin at me wiv eyes like chapel 'atpegs: He's staring at me.

'Ey! You wiv de nose on your face!: Hey there!

'Ey you, make your name walker: Perhaps you wouldn't mind leaving.

Gerroff arr'Edge 'ill: Coitus interruptus (Edge Hill being the penultimate station before Lime Street).

Gisalite: May I have a light, please?

Go on, la; you cudden knock de skin off a rice puddin: You can try, but you will not succeed.

Ir'll take a man, norris shert butt'n: You are not up to this.

Jesus, it's cold enough for two bloody bootlaces: It's rather chilly.

Muck in, la, you're at your Grannie's: Please partake of as much as you like.

She's gorrup de jigger eyes: She has that certain indefinable attraction.

Ta wacker, I'll mug yew an all when I'm carryin': Thank you so much, I will return the complement when I have the means.

Yer judy's gob's like a parish oven: Your young lady talks rather a lot, doesn't she?

Yew an ooh else?: Just you try.

Yew dancin', or wha'?: May I have the next dance, please?

Yews can buggeroff, I'm wiv me owl feller: Thank you for asking, but I can't, I'm with my husband.

The 'Tunny'

Tunnel Road

Edge Hill Station

To Town

Swimming Baths Library

SW Tram Stop

Upper Parliament Street

Smithdown Road

Kingsley Road

Alt Street

Solway Arms

The Brick

Rialto

Tiber Street School

Croxteth Park Cemetery

To Woolton Woods

Bombed Site

Lodge Lane

No. 43 Tagus St

Prince's Road

Croxteth Road

Ullet Road

Old Nick's Cave

Prince's Park

Old Farm Field Peter Pan

Sefton Park

Cafe Theatre

Fairy Glen

Iron Bridge

Band Stand

Dingle

Aigburth Road

Boat Lake

12

Tagus Street family & friends

Mid pleasures and palaces though we may roam,
Be it ever so humble, there's no place like home.

(*Home, Sweet Home*, THOMAS LOVE PEACOCK)

'PLEASE MISSIS HAYTER, your Kenny's shit his pants.'

Terry stood on the pavement in front of the doorstep of No. 43 and announced the event in a matter-of-fact way to my mother. He stood waiting for instructions, his round face impassive and his hands stuffed into the remains of pockets in his grubby grey short flannel pants. Terry's pants, much patched, were the top half of his older brother's long trousers cut down when the knees got threadbare: baggy round the legs, voluminous about his waist and held up by red and green striped braces.

Tagus Street, like all of its neighbours, was so narrow that a hop, skip and a jump across its tarred cobbles took you from one side to the other

13

My mother completely ignored him and continued her conversation with a small group of neighbours clustered around our front door.

It was the summer of 1945 and she was leaning on our railings, airing her views on where Mrs Green got all her tinned fruit from when there was almost nothing in the shops; and what there was, was rationed. She put her cigarette back on the end of her lower lip, then stabbed the doorstep with her brush to emphasise her disgust with the tactics used by her absent neighbour to supplement her groceries.

Terry, only half listening and not really understanding, gathered that it had something to do with Mr Green being away in the army overseas, and a contingent of American soldiers who were living somewhere in Upper Parliament Street.

Terry, though only six at the time, was wise in the ways of gossiping women; his mother was renowned at the art, and so he remained patiently silent, studying his feet.

He wore no socks and wiggled his big right toe in an attempt to speed up its exit through a hole in his black canvas gym pumps, also cast off from his brother and several sizes too big. Terry bent down and rubbed an angry

'all the Nazi bombers did was to turn a lot of useless buildings into a paradise of bombed sites for us to play on, for we were too young to understand'

red bruise on his shin with the cuff of his open-necked, once-white shirt.

'Not again, where is he?' My mother suddenly turned on Terry, her cigarette jiggling up and down in rhythm with the question.

Terry almost shot out of his skin; engrossed as he was with the bruise on his leg and his big toe.

'Tell our Kenneth I'll batter him when I get my 'ands on him. Now where is he?'

She returned to the subject of Mrs Green and her relationship with American soldiers.

This left Terry somewhat nonplussed and he pondered his dilemma for a few seconds. If he told her where I was hiding, I would be rescued from my plight, but battered; and I might decide to seek revenge on him: I was one year older, and one year makes a difference when you are six years old. On the other hand, if he didn't tell he would probably still get battered: a mother's influence in those days spread well beyond her own offspring to any delinquent urchin in the neighbourhood. Having thought it out, he decided it was in my best interest to tell. In any case watching me suffer had a certain attraction, even if I was his best friend.

'Your Kenny's in the jigger at the bottom of the street Missis Hayter; same place as last time,' he said, his affected air of disinterest belied by a look of smug satisfaction at what I was about to suffer.

And so it was, that despite his occasional relapse into sadism, Terry, with Billy and his brother Georgie who lived just across the street, and Tommy who lived further down towards the bombed site, were inseparable best friends throughout my childhood in the war years of Liverpool 8.

Billy was the oldest member of our gang, renowned for his extensive knowledge of pain and suffering, gained from the constant practise of inflicting them on his younger brother Georgie, and from avid reading of American horror comics. Not very tall for his age, Billy was sturdily built, with a ruddy face topped by a mop of gingery-brown hair.

He always dressed casually: his summer attire was usually a striped short-sleeved shirt kept in place with two or three buttons and a safety pin, its tail hanging out over black short trousers bunched and held around the waist by a snake-clasped belt. His stocky legs were encased in much darned grey socks, one crumpled around his ankle, the other worn just below the knee and kept there by turning over the top. The socks were stuffed into enormous black boots.

Winter attire was exactly the same, except that it was all hidden under a voluminous overcoat trailing along the ground, whilst his head and face were protected from the cold by a woollen balaclava with one eye hole bigger than the other, and an unstable bobble on top.

15

Georgie was almost as tall as his brother, though of slimmer build and a little fairer in complexion, but with a similar mop of hair as a result of their mother using the same basin for both of their hair-cuts. He was not destined to become another Einstein, but he was happy with his lot, always smiling, even when he was under assault from Billy.

Georgie seldom wore anything other than a woolly striped pullover tucked into short grey trousers held up by yellow and blue braces. For some reason or other, his shins were always either bruised and bleeding, or scabby from a recent wound, or both; not helped by his aversion to wearing socks. A pair of once white plimsolls with holes in the uppers completed his ensemble.

Tommy was the youngest in the gang and came from a family with even less money than the rest of us. His mother did the best for him that she could by acquiring an assortment of clothes from a variety of sources, including the local rag-and-bone man. This often meant that he was either immersed in billowing shirts and trousers, and tattered shoes many sizes too big, or, on the odd occasion, barefoot, with his thin chest and rickety legs exposed to the elements and the scorn of the local kids.

Accepting his poverty, Tommy always seemed perfectly contented with his lot. He never complained, seeming grateful for what he had, particularly for the patronage of Billy.

Despite Billy's tendency to take advantage of anyone smaller or weaker than himself, he had a soft spot for Tommy and acted as his protector. There was a strange understanding between them, and Tommy's pale face would light up when he met Billy, whilst Billy round face, with its habitual threatening scowl, would widen into a broad smile.

There were dozens of other children living in Tagus, Tiber, Ritson, Ashbridge and the other streets off Lodge Lane: families tended to be large in those days. They all touched our lives, but it was Terry, Billy, Georgie and Tommy who were the most important characters in my world, apart, of course, from my family.

My mam, whose name was Martha or sometimes May, was a little lady of five foot nothing, slim of build, with dark auburn hair and piercing brown eyes. She shouted a lot and threatened more, but did nothing except to nurture and to love my brother Charlie and me: no mean task in those days of little money, with everything rationed and two forever hungry juvenile delinquents.

I now realise that she was a very intelligent and shrewd woman, as well-read as Lodge Lane Public Library would allow, devouring the works of A. J. Cronin and Mazo de la Roche, whilst working steadily along the library's history shelves.

Mam's favourite colour was green; and when contrast was required, she added dark green, though brown was sometimes an acceptable alternative. Everything in the house suitable for painting was painted green or brown, except the brass ornaments and even they were tinged green with dried Brasso. Her colour preference extended to her choice in clothes and, with her brown hair, it was sometimes hard to make her out against the background décor.

Even when various shades of nylon stockings became available, hers stayed an uncompromising thick brown: green being one of the colours not available.

Handbags and heavy topcoats were an infrequently indulged passion: worn once then stored, when she would complain she had nothing to wear.

There's nothing more that needs to be said about my mam. She was my mother and I loved her; and she loved my elder brother Charlie and me.

She loved us to the point where we could do no wrong, despite the constant flow of evidence to the contrary, and the occasional visit from the local bobby. Mind you, I did wonder on occasions, whether she had delegated the job of inflicting punishment on me, to Charlie, for he seemed to do it fairly frequently and apparently at random. But when we got older he took pains to assure me that it was not Mam who told him to do it, he did it quite spontaneously, especially when there was not much else to do.

Kenneth 'Spud' Hayter was born the year the Second World War was started, six years after Charlie, or, to give him his full title, Our Kid, or otherwise, Charles Herbert Hayter.

Until the war ended, there were just the three of us: Mam, Charlie and me. There was the occasional reference to someone called a father, but he was away somewhere, serving in the armed forces, so I wasn't quite sure what he had to do with us.

When the war was over, we suddenly got a dad. He arrived home one day, sat down by the wireless, turned it on and stayed there for the rest of his life.

So that was the immediate family: me, Charlie, my brother, Mam and a person who arrived on a permanent basis after the war had ended, called Dad.

Dad, it seems, had signed on for the Air Force just before the war started, when Charlie was six and I was zero plus a bit.

The rules of engagement for the Second World War were that, if you volunteered, you had some choice as to which of the services you joined, and where you would be stationed. He couldn't swim, so that ruled out the Royal Navy as far as he was concerned. Soldiers carried guns and

17

MAM AND DAD

She was a very intelligent and shrewd woman: as well read as Lodge Lane Public Library would allow. When the war was over, we suddenly got a Dad. He arrived home one day, sat down by the wireless, turned it on and stayed there for the rest of his life

sometimes got close enough to the enemy to use them, and he reasoned that the enemy might resent getting shot at, and shoot back. So the Army was out.

This persuaded Dad to join the Air Force, and having decided on the Air Force the next thing was to ensure his feet stayed firmly on the ground. It wasn't so much the thought of flying that bothered him, more the idea that the Germans might not like him being up there and do something about it. This meant failing any test that otherwise might mean him getting airborne. Showing great determination and applying all his intellectual talent, Dad never got more than two out of ten in anything.

Then there was the choice of RAF station. Here, the problem was Hitler: what were the Führer's long term invasion plans?

Dad probably borrowed a map of Europe and a copy of Mein Kampf, before deciding on Ireland. Ireland was his home for the first five years of my life, though it seems he showed his unswerving devotion to his family by sending an occasional gift of a bar of chocolate or an army blanket to Mam, but rarely risking a visit. Hitler might have U-boats lurking in the Irish Sea and he told Mam that he was worried about what would happen to her if he was targeted. Quite what Mam thought of this dreadful prospect, nobody knew.

Because we hardly ever saw him, I never realised that he had anything permanently to do with us, particularly as both he and Mam always cheered up when it was time for him to go back to fighting for his country, after a visit to us.

It was some time after the war was over and he had resided with us for a few months, before it dawned on me that he was here to stay with Charlie, Mam and me; and I resented Hitler for packing up so soon.

To be fair, he never interfered too much: adopting an aloof approach to his parental duties by leaving everything remotely connected to his offspring's welfare to Mam.

Dad was rather slight of build but with jet black hair and a liking for smart dressing. I suppose he must have been a handsome man; and maybe that's why Mam married him, because it was difficult to think of any other reason. Mind you, he was something of an intellect; at least, he believed himself to be something of an intellect, and proved it by listening to the Brains Trust on the wireless, every week without fail.

Next to Dick Barton, Special Agent, and Wilfred Pickles, the Brains Trust was his favourite programme and every episode had him disagreeing violently with Professor Huxley.

Dad destroyed Huxley's views with cold logic partly derived from his works of reference, the Reader's Digest; but mainly with his searching assessment of the Professor's IQ: 'Thinks 'e's a bloody know-all 'e does, Professor Know-all's worr'e thinks 'e is. Professor Knowsbuggerall is more like it.' He would interject at the crucial point in the debate, thus destroying Huxley's argument.

Mam, who followed some of the debate on the programme,

CHARLIE AND BABY ME

Not very tall, but lanky and six years older than I, he wielded power over me at every opportunity: that is to say every time I was within reach and Mam wasn't

19

would say nothing; there was no point: any views she might air would be destroyed with the same devastating logic.

Mind you, I do sometimes wonder if Dad was more of an intellect than he was given credit for; because he did come out with some pretty telling philosophical observations from time to time. I recall one such occasion, when I was grown up and he was very ill in hospital. It was from his sick bed that he uttered something so profound that Descartes would surely have wished he had thought of it first.

Dad really did think he was going to die and so did his visitors, clustered expectantly around his bed.

Charlie and I had got there at the start of visiting time and Dad was either asleep or unconscious. Mam arrived half an hour later with Uncle Walter and Aunty Mabel, blaming their late arrival on the difficulty of getting served in the Coach and Horses on Lodge Lane.

'Looks a lot paler than yesterday, May,' Aunty Mabel observed cheerfully, leaning over the bed to get a closer look. 'Is 'e still with us?' she asked nervously, leaning closer to the deathly pale figure to check the absence of breathing.

Dad coughed.

Aunty Mabel shot backwards, frantically trying to get distance between herself and the resurrection. She clung hold of Mam. 'Jesus Christ, May. He frightened the bloody life out of me!' she gasped. 'Christ Almighty, I nearly died of bloody fright, the bloody sod! I thought he'd gone!' She glared at the ex-corpse.

The commotion woke Dad up and he surveyed his well wishers, his eyes moving from one to another. 'I hope I don't go to heaven,' he said, faintly.

'Now don't talk like that,' Mam said, finishing off the last of the cigarettes Charlie had brought for Dad the day before. 'What'll the nurses think, saying things like that? In any case, you'll be going the other bloody way, so don't worry. Anyway, why don't you want to go to heaven?'

It was then that Dad uttered a profound philosophical comment on man's destiny.

He raised himself on one elbow and fixed his eyes on each of us in turn.

'Because I don't wanna spend eternity all by me bloody self!' he replied.

Charlie was somewhat fairer in complexion than Dad. Not very tall, but lanky and six years older than I, he wielded power over me at every opportunity: that is to say every time I was within reach and Mam wasn't. Fortunately, the difference in ages was such that he had a different set of mates, and seldom did our paths cross outside the house. In the house, I was fairly safe because either Mam was in too, or she might appear at any minute.

ME AND CHARLIE

To be fair, there were other good points in having an older brother ... On very rare occasions, he showed a glimmer of brotherly love by taking me fishing with his mates to Prince's Park

However, I must admit he came in handy if anyone else assaulted me: he would go and sort them out. Whilst grateful for his support, I was never sure whether he did it for the honour of the family, because he wanted to protect me or because he resented anyone else inflicting pain on me. Whatever the reason, 'I'll tell our Charlie on you!' was my best form of defence.

To be fair, there were other good points in having an older brother like Charlie: he provided endless supplies of American comics and cast-off long trousers to be cut down to my short ones; and I had covert access to his bike and cricket bat. On very rare occasions, he showed a glimmer of brotherly love by taking me fishing with his mates to Prince's Park.

Not only that, but Charlie had sent a cut-out coupon from one of his DC Comics all the way to America and had become one of the few English members of the exclusive Superman Club. His Membership Card and tin badge enabled me to bask in the radiance of his fame as the only known member of the Superman Club in Liverpool 8.

Contact between Charlie and me was mainly physical, of the assault kind, and seldom verbal, except again of the assault kind. He never showed any interest in my activities; nor did he share any of his secrets with me, except once.

We slept in the same room, which had two iron-framed single beds against opposite walls, a large wardrobe and a dressing table with a big mirror on it.

One particular night I was already in bed, bundled up warmly in a collection of army blankets, with the added luxury of Dad's overcoat over the bottom of the bed to keep my feet warm. Charlie was hanging around half undressed and obviously had something on his mind.

I had just formed a cosy hollow in the flock mattress and closed my eyes, when Charlie stood up and walked over to the dressing table.

"Ey you!' he addressed his sleepy little brother. 'You asleep or what?'

The Sandman ran for cover and I peered over the blankets, wondering what had prompted an assault at bedtime.

Charlie was standing in front of the mirror in his underpants and vest, staring at the ceiling.

'I'm thinking of being a bally dancer when I gerrout of school,' he announced. "Ow-about that then?'

Charlie, for the first time in his life, seemed interested in my opinion. The trouble was I didn't know what a Bally Dancer was; but I couldn't let the opportunity of helping Charlie with his career go by. 'I wouldn't mind bein' one of them as well Charlie,' I encouraged him. 'Worris it?'

Charlie transferred his gaze from the ceiling to the lower form of life in bed.

'It's a Bally Dancer, he ballies about, dancin'. Are you thick or somethin? He ballies about to classicable music.'

I was none the wiser, but tried to look knowledgeable, now that the whole thing had been explained to me.

'He ballies about in tight clothes and throws girls up in the air and runs around and jumps up and down on a stage with his toes stuck out,' he continued with growing excitement. 'And he gets to meet the nobs an' 'e drives a big car.'

I began to think that this ballying wasn't such a bad idea. Throwing girls up in the air had a certain attraction, after all Charlie didn't say you had to catch them on the way down; and whilst I wasn't sure about the nobs bit, driving a big car was a definite plus.

It seems that Charlie had read a story in one of his comics about a young man who had always dreamed of becoming a famous Ballet Dancer; and the description of the youth exactly fitted what Charlie imagined was his lithe physique.

The whole thing had fired Charlie's ambition: no longer would a Private Investigator's job do; nor a Test Cricketer. Charlie wanted to be a Ballet Dancer: fêted by aristocracy all over the world, and the driver of big cars.

'Well worrer you think about that then?' he demanded, turning towards the mirror.

'Great that, Charlie, can I be one when you're one?' I pleaded. 'When are you going to start?'

The dancer in the story had practised for years and years, starting as a young boy in the slums of the East End of London; so Charlie realised he had better get cracking; after all he was eleven.

'I'm startin' tonight and I'm gunner practise every day an' gerra job in London as soon as I leave school,' Charlie replied.

Without further ado, and surveying the effect in the dressing table mirror, he rose up on tiptoe with hands stretched high above his head.

I watched the first steps to stardom in awe: particularly fascinated by the slow descent of his underpants.

'You 'aven't gorra girl to throw about,' I cautioned.

'I know that,' said Charlie, his face going red with exertion and irritated by the interruption. 'I'm startin' with the jumping up and down bit.'

Intent on making progress on the steps illustrated in his comic, Charlie pranced about then started jumping up and down with his toes pointing down and his arms raised high.

His underpants descended a further inch or two.

Clearly satisfied with progress, he tried a few straight leg hops, sideways. Each jump left the underpants lagging behind a bit, whilst the cotton legs flapped gracefully round his knees.

His first practice was going better than he had dared hope and he was already up to page two in the story. Charlie decided on a straight leg jump with a simultaneous twist of the feet.

The effect was spectacular. Charlie rose two feet but his underpants stayed put, then dropped around his ankles, cascading gently to the floor.

Charlie followed less gently.

There was a resounding 'thump' as he hit the lino in a tangled heap, followed by an anguished cry from Charlie. Two skinny legs and a bare bottom thrashed about in a desperate bid to extricate himself from his underpants and regain poise more suited to a star of the Royal Ballet.

'What the sodden 'ell are you doin' up there?' The roar from Dad downstairs put paid to any further ballying that night, and just in time: I was in some danger of being heard under the bedclothes, a blanket stuffed in my mouth, convulsed with helpless laughter.

For the record, Charlie never did confide in me again; nor did he ever dance *Swan Lake*, having later decided on a career as a bricklayer.

I was five years old at the end of the war, somewhat tall for my age, and with a basin haircut.

Mam did her best to keep me clothed, performing minor miracles with Charlie's outgrown long trousers: reducing them down to short ones, making sure I never grew out of them before they disintegrated, by cutting them below knee level. Charlie's outgrown shirts and jumpers provided the rest of my wardrobe. The only things of my own were my shoes: black canvas pumps, because Charlie's wore out before he could pass them on.

Everything I wore was too big for me: there was more of clothes than there was of me. Uncle George used to look me up and down and say to Mam, 'Christ, May, has young Charlie shrunk again? He would then dissolve into laughter, with me peering balefully over the folds of Charlie's cast-off jumper.

I used to pray to Jesus to ask him to make Charlie stop growing so I could overtake him and proffer my hand-me-downs to him. That way he'd end up with his own clothes back, third hand.

This then, was my immediate family: Mam, Charlie, someone called Dad, and me. We lived in No. 43 Tagus Street, off Lodge Lane, Liverpool 8, one of a row of identical red-brown brick terraced 'two-up, two-downs'.

The houses squatted, facing their twins across a narrow street, each with a sash bay bedroom window sitting above an identical parlour window, with the front door to one side. Their front doors were one step away from the slate pavements edged at the road by granite slabs, forming the gutters, and the roadway between the rows of houses was paved with grey-black granite blocks set in black tar.

'Two up, two down' was not strictly true, because every house had a tiny kitchen and an outside lav' in the backyard. The lav' seemed to be Dad's favourite place, next to the chair by the wireless. His days off work and when he wasn't playing bowls or watching the football in Sefton Park were busy and well organised. Daylight hours were spent in the chair listening to the wireless, followed by an hour or so in the early evening in the lav', reading the *Liverpool Echo* right from the title through the adverts to Gussy Goose, the cartoon, then back to the chair until bedtime.

There was a time when I thought the outside lav' had some religious significance. The idea stemmed from the fact that my knowledge of the Scriptures was a bit skimpy but I was going to Sunday School at the time. Mam was forever shouting down the yard to Dad, "Ey you, for Christ's sake hurry up. God knows, you've been down there long enough. Serves you right if your tea's burnt to a cinder! And it's the last time I'm telling you!'

I vaguely connected this to some holy presence in the lav' with Dad, and a story about some king or other burning the cakes for the Last Supper with Jesus.

Despite the drab sameness of the little terraced houses, there was no sameness about the families who lived in them. Apart from anything else, those who lived at the top of the street, between Ocklershaw's sweet shop, in the middle of the street, and Lodge Lane, were all 'tu'pence-ha'penny

Backyard No. 43, Tagus Street

snobs', according to those who lived at the other end of the street. It seems that those who lived at the top end were slightly less destitute than those at the bottom.

One family was black. They were well-to-do, in comparison with most of our neighbours, and lived near the top of the street. The grandfather was once a tribal chief in Africa, according to their close neighbours. According to those at the other end of the street, he was a navvy working on the docks until he won on Littlewoods. Apart from 'Grandad Moneybags', as he was known, there was his daughter, her husband who went to work in a suit, and their son of about my age. The son suffered much in our hands because of his name. His Christian name was Dickie, and his surname, Balls.

The only other suit of sorts belonged to Mr Jones. It was his postman's uniform until he lost it with his job when he was sacked for stealing Postal Orders out of letters, and sealing the envelope up again.

He must have done it for years before someone in authority realised all the missing postal orders were missing from letters delivered by Mr Jones.

When he was sacked, Mam gave to a street collection to help him out.

25

There was much discussion, at the time, as to how best to get your hands on other people's money: was it better to take it out of the envelope and then throw the envelope away, or seal it up again? On balance, most agreed on the throwing it away method, because Jonesy had tried the sealing up system and he had got caught.

I remember no debate on the morals of what he had done, only the method.

One family even had a car: a battered old black Morris used only on Sundays to go to Church. It seems the man of the house, who was very religious, had 'something to do' with the Church.

'Pinching lead off the bloody roof,' according to Mrs Callaghan. 'That's how 'e got the bloody car.'

The top end of the street had fewer houses than the bottom end because almost opposite No. 43, occupying most of the street to the top, was Tiber Street School for mixed infants and 'Seniors'. 'Too much mixing from some of them, if you ask me, specially the seniors,' Mam used to say, 'dirty little buggers.'

I never knew what she meant, but our Charlie looked a bit sheepish.

Lodge Lane, 'Lodgy', a once prosperous road of shops, ran along the top of Tagus Street, one of many just like it, running into Lodgy. Lodge Lane stretched between the crossed roads of Smithdown and Tunnel Road at one end, to Croxteth at the other, not far from the Lodge House of Sefton Park.

When all the possibilities of the bombed sites at the bottom of the street, the 'debbies', had been exhausted, 'Sevvy' Park was a much loved alternative playground for the kids from miles around.

The bottom of Tagus and adjacent streets had no real end; they just sort of spread out into a number of bombed sites with houses and shops only half demolished, the result of the 'Gerries' trying to destroy our docks and the Pier Head. But all the Nazi bombers did was to turn a lot of useless buildings into a paradise of bombed sites for us to play on, for I was too young to understand what the destruction meant to others. Despite the bombs, the City survived and so did the dogged humour of its Scousers. As a song of much later recalled, '... and when all the dust and the smoke had all cleared; thank God said the old man, the Pier Head's still there!'

A maze of streets and back entries spread out from the bombed sites, and, if you knew the way and ignored our mams' instructions not to go, the streets and jiggers led eventually to the city shops and the docks of the Pool. They also led to the next best thing to Sevvy Park: Prince's Park, 'Prinny' to us.

The streets off Lodge Lane were each a tiny community, where everybody knew everybody else. There was an intangible something that caused the neighbours to be there if they were needed, to give a little something to those with less, without being asked, and without wanting a 'thank you'. There seemed no need to ask and no need to offer.

But nobody was spared the innuendo and, sometimes, outright slander of gossiping women. There was only one way to avoid being talked about, and that was to join in with the gossip. It was a brave woman who was first to leave a group of women, chattering in front of one of the houses, on their way to do the shopping on Lodge Lane.

Our house seemed to be a favourite to gather, perhaps because it still had its railings to lean on.

No. 43 sprouted a row of cast iron railings just in front of its small bay window, and between us and next door's step. Most of the arrow-like railings on other houses had disappeared just before I was born, for 'the war effort'. It seems most available iron was collected and melted down to make guns and the weapons of war. I was about five years old when I heard Charlie in deep discussion with his pals, demanding to know how we were supposed to win the war '…when the Germans 'ave got bloody great tanks and airyplanes, an' all we've got is cast iron bloody arrows.'

We were doomed, I decided; and went out to play.

The railings protruded from sandstone slabs which recorded, for posterity, the initials of all the kids for miles around; comments on who did not have a father, and who loved who and what they'd done to show their love.

The '3' in our number '43' disappeared from our door at about the same time as our neighbours' railings disappeared, but this was more likely to be the work of Terry on tiptoe than the war effort.

All of the front doors in the street, as far as I remember, were either some shade of brown, or, like ours, a nondescript hue of green, a green unique to front doors and certainly never seen in nature.

Apart from the '4', the only other decoration was an ornate cast iron letterbox complete with heavy knocker. This was an essential piece of apparatus, whether for summoning us from the inner depths of the house, posting letters and the *Liverpool Echo*, or just banging on and running away.

Our front door, like all our neighbours', gave way to the lobby, a narrow passage leading to the other rooms, whose sole source of light was a small fanlight above the door. The floor of the dimly lit lobby was covered with well-worn brown lino portraying the remains of a mock woodblock pattern; whilst the ceiling, pretending to be supported by chunks of plaster cast in the style of crude Roman pillars, was whitewashed. Faded paper, patterned

27

with intertwined roses and cornflowers, covered the walls, except for a foot or so above the skirting board where it had been systematically removed by Tibby our cat, sharpening her claws for the next encounter with Mrs Callaghan's ginger tom. Straight ahead from the door were the stairs leading to the bedrooms, and just before the stairs two doors led off to the left: the first to the parlour and the other to our living room.

Charlie and I were hardly ever allowed into the parlour because 'it's for entertaining', Mam would insist; but when we were, we wondered what all the fuss was about. It was spotlessly clean but all it had in it was an old settee, a couple of chairs and a black wooden carved table that Uncle Charlie had brought back from Africa when he came home on leave from the Army.

Despite Mam's insistence that the parlour was for entertaining visitors, I can't actually remember us ever having visitors of the sort you entertained. We had plenty of aunts, uncles and neighbours coming to see us, but they went straight into the living room. The only others visitors were people like the rent collector or the cheque man and they never got past the front door, if, by rare mistake, it was opened for them.

Our living room was the centre of all life and its focus was the black shiny cast iron grate, with its hob and oven, which Mam religiously black-leaded every Sunday morning. A mantlepiece over the grate displayed two chalk dogs, one at either end, glaring belligerently at each other over the Westminster Chime clock with its temperamental chimes and loose minute finger.

It was this loose finger that was nearly the death of a regular visitor of the family type: Uncle Walter.

Uncle Walter was my mother's younger brother and he was married to Aunty Mabel. It seems Mabel had known Walter since he was a child, and from the age of ten she had him marked down as her future husband, the moment he reached the age of consent. Walter was not consulted on the matter.

She lived, and he existed, in a tiny first floor flat above a butcher in the Dingle, not far from the south-end docks and half an hour's walk from our house. Uncle Walter was meek and quiet-mannered by nature. Small and thin of stature, he always looked ill. He was so quiet and unobtrusive that we never really got to know him. He never actually seemed to be there somehow and so, like Aunty Mabel did, we tended to ignore him.

You couldn't, however, ignore Aunty Mabel. She was definitely there and you knew about it. She was the complete opposite to Uncle Walter. Five foot eleven in height and twice that in circumference, she always wore a faded green dress with big red flowers all over it. Three or four inches of

Dock Road, one of the bomb sites that we considered to be paradise!

grubby-white, threadbare underskirt hung provocatively below the hem of her dress and the ensemble was completed by scuffed and battered black leather shoes.

The more inquisitive and less discerning observers of ladies' ankles might just catch a glimpse of rumpled sixty denier brown stockings with ladders in them, if they waited for the underskirt to ride up a bit, which it did with alarming results whenever she sat down.

I once overheard Mam telling Mrs Williams of the evening when Aunty Mabel had noticed one such observer in the public bar of The Brick, her local when she visited us:

''Ey you, you dirty old bugger!' she shouted across to the other side of the bar. 'Who the 'ell d'you think you're lookin' at? 'Aven't you seen a lady before? Dirty sod, you keep your bloody eyes to yourself! Ought to 'ave it cut off. There's no sodden peace for ladies nowadays. Dirty old sods like 'im lookin' at respectable ladies' legs. A lady's not safe nowhere nowadays, is she May? If my Walter was 'ere, 'e'd do you!'

She turned from her admirer to my mother. The object of Aunty Mabel's wrath looked behind him: there was nobody there.

'What the 'ell's that fat old bag on about?' he muttered to himself, before returning to his study of next Saturday's Aintree runners, in the *Echo*.

My mother said nothing, but sipped her glass of Guinness and tried to

29

work out who Mabel was referring to when she mentioned a lady: ladies were infrequent visitors to the public bar at The Brick.

At the opposite end to Aunty Mabel's ankles, great ham-like arms stretched the dress beyond its limit, and a bull neck, thrusting apart the neckline, supported a big ruddy face with all kinds of folds on it and a few warty growths with hairs sticking out. But her blotchy red face was lovely: not the pretty kind of lovely, even the opposite; but it beamed laughter. Or, if it wasn't laughing, it was smiling; and to kids, smiling faces are lovely faces.

The whole of Aunty Mabel was topped by greying mousey hair, which she kept short and never touched, except with a very fine metal comb when she had to.

'I keeps it short 'cause of the nits,' she would say wisely. 'You can't comb 'em out propl'y with long hair, can you May?'

Mam would say nothing, but she was tempted to suggest Mabel might like to try drowning them occasionally in a drop of soapy water, like the rest of the world did.

It's hard to describe Uncle Walter as there was not that much of him to describe; but I do remember he wore a suit that had seen better days, much creased and shiny at the elbows, set off by a crumpled tie, decorated with red spots and gravy stains.

The tie went round a collar twice his size, then down his shirtfront, whilst the end was tucked firmly in his trousers. Uncle Walter always walked along staring at the pavement, with the tie pulling his collar down below his Adam's Apple. With head down and tie tucked tightly down his trousers, he looked as though he was being towed along by the collar, pulled by someone hidden down his trousers, hauling on his tie.

My mother loved 'our Walter' and saw it as the duty of an elder sister to look after him as best she could, in the face of his imminent demise under the care of Mabel.

'You're too soft with 'im you are May,' Mabel would say, her great podgy hands enveloping a glass of brown ale resting on our table. "E's a bit pale sometimes, but 'e's alright our Walter is.' Mabel sailed through life with a strong belief that if you said something often enough, it was true.

Walter sat on an upright wooden chair in the middle of the living room, his collar pulled down from within his trousers, staring at the lino. He hadn't moved for half an hour and he offered no reaction to Mabel's declaration of his well being.

Mabel continued as though Walter was somewhere else. 'I gives 'im money out of his wages for his tram fares to work and pocket money for his Saturday night out, an' I gives 'im a good home. 'E's quite 'appy, our Walter is.'

Mam made no comment: you gave dogs good homes, and she knew Walter got just enough money for his fare and two pints of mild for his Saturday night out, no more. What she didn't know and what Mabel didn't know, was that anyone who worked in public transport got free fares when they were going to work; and Walter was a tram conductor by profession, so his tram fare was available for other purposes.

Walter's two pints on a Saturday night thus became five. Mabel put his appearance after throwing out time, down to him being a bit of a light-weight. ''E's not able to hold 'is ale, our Walter.'

Walter continued to stare unseeingly at the lino.

Aunty Mabel got up from the table and went to the kitchen to replenish the glass with brown ale; colliding with Walter's chair without even noticing the chair, or him on it. The chair rocked under the onslaught; but Walter's stare never wavered from the floor.

Mam looked fondly at the forlorn figure.

'Would you like a cup of tea, love?' she asked, gently.

The unseen presence down his trousers twitched the tie and the corresponding dip of his head said, 'Yes please'.

Aunty Mabel returned with her glass of beer frothing all over the lino.

'I'm partial to an occasional drink,' Mabel would say to anyone she met.

'On the occasion of anytime someone buys her one,' Mam would say, when Mabel was out of earshot.

'It's for me blood pressure!' Mabel would go on to explain. 'It steadies me down and calms me nerves.'

'Steadies her right down onto her back an' calms her nerves so bloody much she can't gerrup again,' Mam would confirm.

Now I understood why Aunty Mabel kept a succession of bottles of Yate's Australian White Wine in her handbag: it was to take care of any sudden surge of blood pressure, which seemed to happen at three or four minute intervals.

If you ignored Mam's concern about Aunty Mabel's style of caring for Uncle Walter, you couldn't help liking Aunty Mabel, with her bulldozing approach to life's problems and her beaming ruddy face. And you couldn't help liking Uncle Walter too, what there was of him.

Uncle Walter knew nothing of the loose finger on the Westminster chime clock that sat in the middle of our mantelpiece. When the big finger got to just past o'clock, it dropped about twenty minutes, then stopped until the clockwork caught up with it.

One Saturday night Uncle Walter had been to The Brick, and decided to stay at our house rather than go home, mainly because it was unlikely he would make it home. Apart from which, even in his hazy condition, he had

31

worked out that Aunty Mabel might have something to say and do about his lack of funds. That very morning she had given him his tram fares for next week and money for Saturday night's two pints, and he had blown the lot.

Mam collected him at the front door and supported him as far as the settee, in front of the dying fire in the living room. Walter collapsed in a heap with arms and legs spread-eagled, and his mouth wide open.

She smiled fondly at the inert heap. 'Sleep tight, Walter love, at least you look as though you enjoyed yourself tonight, though God help you tomorrow.' She gently stroked his forehead and went to bed.

Woken in the early hours by the loud calls of nature, Walter glanced at the clock. The hand dropped twenty minutes.

Uncle Walter's screams woke the whole household.

Mam dashed downstairs, and Walter grabbed her. 'I've 'ad it, May! Me whole bloody life 'as just flashed before me. I've 'ad it!' He jabbed his finger at the clock, before collapsing back onto the settee as the mild ale re-established its hold.

Even Dad was woken up by the commotion, and he staggered downstairs. 'What the 'ell's up wiv 'im, makin' all that bloody noise?'

'Our Walter's very ill,' Mam sobbed. ''E thinks 'e's going to die. What are we going to do?' Mam and Dad then started to argue about what to do next, ignoring the dying Walter for the time being.

Mam had a vague idea he might have had a heart attack and suggested they should call a doctor. Dad was for waiting until morning. 'Just to make sure. Don't forget Doctor Whatyercallim will charge for coming out at night, an' anyway a Doctor's not much bloody good if 'e's gone for a chop, now is 'e?'

You couldn't argue with Dad's logic. In any case, Mam was unsure about the symptoms of a heart attack, and whether or not they included an open mouth and deafening snores. They decided to wait until morning, and went back to bed. After all, Doctor Nugent charged half-a-crown for night visits, even if they resulted in a death certificate.

Next morning, Uncle Walter was still alive, just.

'Must 'ave been a bad pint,' he declared, faintly, after Mam had forced a cup of tea down him.

'There was a bloody good chance of that!' Mam snapped, but much relieved. 'Considering the number you must have swilled back last night, there's a fair chance one of them was bad.'

Dad was also relieved because, as he said when Uncle Walter had gone home, 'Bloody good job he didn't go for a chop. Bet the miserable sod isn't insured; and we'd have 'ad to find the money to plant 'im.'

Our living room was over-furnished with a square table and chairs, a settee, sideboard and an easy chair, which almost matched the settee. The brown lino in the lobby ended just under the door, giving way to green with cream squares covering the whole of the living room floor. An oblong rug in front of the grate added a touch of luxury. Dad had made the rug by laboriously poking multi-coloured strips of assorted rags through the weave of a carefully cut oblong piece of sacking; the back of which proclaimed the quality of Tate & Lyle sugar.

The room was so lived in, that the faint light provided by a single small window overlooking the backyard made it cosy rather than gloomy. It was a sash window but as far as I know, had never been opened. In fact, it was wedged into its frame by wads of newspaper 'to keep out the draughts', and covered by generations of paint.

A single mantle gaslight and the coal fire in a cast iron range provided our night-time illumination, making the living room even more cosy during the long winter nights. We ate, we played and we listened to the wireless in that room. It was the centre of our lives.

A latched door opened from the living room into a tiny kitchen, which again had a window and a gaslight.

Part of the kitchen was a narrow wedge formed by the underneath of the stairs at the end of the lobby. We called it the larder, but it was left clear except for a yard brush, a step ladder, the shoe cleaning box and other assorted essential junk.

Mam kept it reasonably clear out of habit, because during the war, someone in authority on the wireless had instructed families to hide under the stairs when the Luftwaffe was bombing them, this being perfectly safe, according to the wireless broadcast, if you didn't have a handy air-raid shelter.

Mam was patriotic and did not question authority, though she did wonder why Churchill operated from a massive underground concrete fortress, when under the stairs at No. 10 Downing Street was just as good.

A brown painted wooden cabinet housed our crockery and cutlery, such as it was, together with floor cloths and blocks of sandstone and donkey stone for the front door step. Food was kept in a similar cabinet with a wire mesh door to keep it fresh, with a mousetrap left just outside, permanently set in case someone left the door open. The idea, I suppose, was to trap the robber before it had time to eat the stolen food and so return it to the cabinet. The trap had about as much effect on No. 43's rodent population as Tibby, our cat.

To be fair, Tibby was a bedraggled sixty-three in cat years and the mice could outrun him, so they ignored him. However, he did have a fair measure of success with cockroaches and was often found noisily crunching them, usually when we were eating our tea.

Wooden planks forming shelves, supported by brackets nailed into the joints of the bricks along one wall, provided the only other storage facility, but the brackets were so far apart that everything put onto the shelves caused a dangerous sag.

'You'd think 'e'd 'ave done something about them, wouldn't you?' Mam addressed nobody in particular, as she watched a jar of jam put on the end of the shelf slide slowly to the middle. Dad, who was listening intently to the umpteenth episode of Dick Barton Special Agent on the wireless, ignored her.

'Lazy sod. Now that Mr Jones, he'd a' done something. It's like a palace his house is. Mr Jones' shelves have got lino on them.'

'How do you know what 'is 'ouse is like, anyway?' Dad muttered, never shifting his eyes from the wireless.

Mam coloured slightly, murmured something about 'lazy sod' again, and hurriedly disappeared into the backyard to bring in the washing.

'Would you bloody believe it: bloody accumulator's going again; just as Dick Barton was going to thump a Nazi spy. Would you bloody sodden-well believe it! 'Ey Ken, go and get it charged up before they shut!' Dad shouted.

The wireless ran off an accumulator, an acid-filled glass jar battery; and this had to be recharged fairly often. It was my job to take it to Duffy's, the wireless shop on Lodge Lane, to exchange it for a fully charged one. I looked forward to the errand, because it gave me the chance to pour a bit of the acid out and add to half a jam jar full which I kept hidden in the backyard.

One of Charlie's American Comics had a story in it about some acid being used to put Batman and Robin's Batmobile out of action. I reckoned my jam jar would give the German tanks something to think about when the Nazis invaded, which Charlie claimed they would do any time now. One thing was for sure, the jam jar would give them more problems than a few cast iron railings, any day.

A stone sink with a great brass cold tap, a defunct cast iron boiler and a brown speckled enamelled cooker completed the kitchen. The cooker was much favoured by Tibby the cat as a warm place to sleep when the gas was out. She gave it up for a short time after she had curled up on a baking tin full of cinder toffee that Mam had just finished making. It took about half an hour to get her free, and even then, she left bunches of fur behind. The problem was getting the toffee off Tibby's under-parts without wasting too much. Some of it was a bit difficult to eat afterwards, but at least it was not wasted, and the hairs seemed to make it last longer.

Our kitchen was also the bathroom on a Saturday night. Charlie went in first, because it was his job to fetch the bath. I was next in before Charlie's water went too cold, and Mam and Dad followed in succession with a fresh bath-full of hot water: my job being to boil up the water in three huge pans; two on the stove, and one on the fire.

To complete the tour of the downstairs of No. 43, you opened a door in the kitchen and stepped out into the backyard where Charlie went for the bath, an oval shaped tin tub, hanging on the wall opposite the kitchen door. The yard was paved with cracked quarry tiles and contained the outside toilet and lean-to wooden coal shed, all protected by a six-foot high wall. Charlie and I had made a garden by digging up a row of tiles. A green privet and fern managed to survive the dust and smoke, and the attentions of Tibby.

The only other greenery tough enough to survive the dusty air and Tibby was next door's creeper, cascading over our side of the wall.

Mam did try to expand the garden by regularly planting marigold seeds in a box on the windowsill. The shoots always appeared in May, but by the end of June they lost the battle for survival in the perpetual shade of the backyard, and shrivelled away. She watered them to the last, then tried again next year.

A clothesline was strung across the yard, handily positioned over the mangle and the dolly tub. Charlie had invented a special 'dare' for anyone he could lure to the mangle. What you had to do was to put your fingers between the rollers of the mangle whilst Charlie turned the handle, the idea being to see how far your fingers would go through the rollers before you screamed for mercy. Whoever got the furthest, won. The fun was usually brought to an end by Mam responding to the screams of some daredevil trying to get his flattened fingers out, whilst Charlie leaned on the handle.

Just behind the lav', in a hole in the wall, hung the dustbin. The lid was inside the yard for putting rubbish in, but the bin was collected by the bin-men from outside, in the narrow jigger running the whole length of the houses and separating our yards from those in the next street.

As regular as clockwork, the bin-men appeared once a week and dumped the bin's contents into their horse-drawn wagon; and very welcome they were, especially to Grandad.

Nin and Grandad Ince lived just down our street on the opposite side to us, in No. 16, and so the layout of the rooms in their house was a mirror image of ours. Their furniture was different though: most of it was in one piece. At least, it was in the living room. What it was like in the parlour and upstairs, I have no idea: Charlie and I were never allowed anywhere except the living room and backyard.

A rather ornate oak sideboard stood against one wall in the living room and contained the family collection of china and crockery, and all the 'important papers': the Rent Book, Grandad's Insurance Policy and the payment book for Freeman's cheques. Grandma Nin's easy chair, Grandad's rocker and three uprights, around a small table, with a spotlessly white, starched lace tablecloth, filled most of the rest of the space.

The only other piece of furniture as such was a bookcase. *Black Beauty*, several works of Dickens, Volumes 1 and 4 of an Encyclopaedia and Gibbons' *The Rise and Fall of the Roman Empire* filled the case and fascinated Charlie and me. In fact, Charlie was probably the only Scouser who had plodded through every page of the Gibbons, looking for rude words, having failed to find any in *Black Beauty* or the works of Dickens.

Above the dresser and hanging on the wall, was the family heirloom: a Granddaughter clock. Sure evidence of its great antiquity was the difference in colour between the wall behind it and that beside it. The clock tick-tocked away the hours to give you some idea whether it was day or night: something that was difficult to determine in Nin's dimly lit living room.

Their house was decorated in the style of an earlier period to ours: ours was late George V and theirs Victorian, which meant that their green and brown paint was a bit darker than our green and brown paint.

Heavy brocade curtains, never drawn more than a few inches apart, discouraged ingress of any of the sun's rays that managed to reach them through the dusty atmosphere. Aided by the décor, the curtains maintained an ambience of permanent gloom. In this perpetual twilight,

NIN

Her face was rounded, well lined and crinkled, and she hardly ever smiled; but we knew she loved us, her children and her grandchildren

*'You'd 'ave to be 'ard, wiv
a nose like that,' his mates
would say, though only
when out of earshot*

it was the heirloom's job to distinguish night from day, whilst its chimes announced when to eat and when to go to bed.

But the light from the ever-burning fire in the black-leaded range added to the glow on Nin's proud face as she shouted her empty threats at Charlie and me, transforming the gloom into an atmosphere of timeless comfort.

Mind you, as far as I was concerned, the living room was only an obstacle to gaining entry to the backyard and there to Grandad's shed. The shed, made by Grandad, using packing cases retrieved from the docks where he sometimes worked, was roofed with tarred felt and painted with countless coats of creosote. It occupied half the backyard.

Providing I sought permission first, I was allowed unrestricted access and full use of anything in it except his set of carpenter's chisels, which were banned from use when Terry made a part amputation of his left thumb when trying to make a spear from an old brush pole. I reckoned we would have got away with it if Terry had shown more control, but he kept shouting and bawling, flicking blood all over the place. Grandad had confiscated the chisels before marching him off to hospital.

Inside, the shed smelt lovely: a pungent mixture of old paint, turps, creosote and coal dust; and next door's cat.

Our various attempts at sledges in the winter and bows and arrows and go carts in the summer were only possible because of the shed, with its Aladdin's collection of tins of nails and jam jars full of all manner of essential oddments.

Me and the rest of the gang spent a lot of time in Grandad's shed for quite a few years, in fact right up to the time when Nin found Terry and Georgie haggling with Henry Green's sister. They were negotiating along the lines, 'I'll show you mine if you show me yours first.'

Nin walked in just as Terry finally agreed to go first.

Uncle George lived with Nin and Grandad, but Uncle Walter, having been dragged off by Aunty Mabel, and Uncle Frank, had got married and had moved out; whilst Uncle Charlie had gone off to be a soldier. My mam had moved out too, when for some mysterious reason, she had married Dad.

Uncle Charlie had gone off to fight in the desert whilst Uncle George and Uncle Frank were kept in England because they were in something called 'reserve occupations'. Uncle George, a slim precise Freemason, always neatly dressed, worked in a factory, whilst Uncle Frank, a severe unsmiling man, was a Clerk at a tobacco warehouse in the docklands. It seems that, according to the War Office, if they had gone off to fight for their country, their country would have come to a grinding halt whilst they were away, and so they were kept safely at home.

Uncle Walter was 'called up' and had a medical, but was declared unfit for active service; so he too had to remain in Blighty. The War Office's assessment of Walter's state of health was confirmed by Aunty Mabel, when she heard their verdict. 'Just my sodden luck! Half of England's going to war and the poor buggers are getting shot, an' 'e's bloody stayin' at home! Just my sodden luck. Mind you, 'e's fit for buggerall, 'e is.'

Grandad worked as a casual labourer on the Docks. In those days, everyone who was a labourer was a casual worker and stood with the rest of their colleagues, every day, outside the dock gates, hoping to be picked for work. If they were one of the lucky ones, it meant they added to the family rations from the money they got and, when nobody was looking, from whatever it was that the ships were unloading that day.

Sometimes Grandad would tell stories to my uncles about the exploits of his mates and what they were supposed to have done. The story always seemed to start with: ''Ave you 'eard this one?' and the audience, sometimes including Charlie and me, would sit back and listen with bated breath.

Most of the tales were lost on me; one being about a Docker going home pushing a wheelbarrow with a sack over it. The Dock Police rushed out and grabbed the man, demanding to know what he had hidden under the sack.

'Nowt!' the Docker replied.

'Nowt? There must be somethin'!' the policeman insisted.

'Well there's nowt to do wiv you in it,' the Docker snapped back.

'Right then!' the Policeman declared. 'You're nicked!' Then, with a cry of triumph, he whipped the sack off the barrow.

The barrow was empty.

'Told you there was nowt,' said the Docker.

Shocked and beaten, the policeman let him go and the Docker continued on home to flog the stolen wheelbarrow.

BIN MEN

Grandad had an allotment on the outskirts of Sevvy Park; and the neat mounds left by the bin-men's horses were his vegetables' main source of nourishment

Grandad had thinning grey hair and a wiry grey moustache. His face was over long and weather beaten, like most Dockers, and his eyes were always moist and red as though he had something in them. But his most recognisable feature was his nose. It started well above his eyebrows and thrust on down the middle of his face until its rounded nobbly end drooped over his moustache: a long purple bulbous growth, embellished with pimples and holes full of blackheads. But Grandad had turned what might be thought of as a somewhat unfortunate feature, into a talking point: 'See that,' he would say, his finger on the end of his nose. 'It can smell a pint of good ale from an 'undred yards, that can.'

If Nin overheard him, she would retort, 'How would it know what ale smelt like a hundred yards away? It spends most of its life submerged in the stuff!'

Grandad always seemed to wear thick cheesecloth shirts needing a separate collar, but instead of a collar, he tied a short woollen scarf around his neck. His heavy woollen trousers were tucked down his socks and the outfit was completed by a massive pair of ex-army boots, spit and polished shiny, every other day. Sitting in the rocking chair in the gloomy homeliness of the living room, inches from the smoking grate, and with a pipe of Battleaxe tobacco clenched in his teeth, he looked just like a Grandad should look. But outside the house, especially at work, he liked to think of himself as a man to be reckoned with, 'a hard man'. 'You'd 'ave to be 'ard, wiv a nose like that,' his mates would say, though only when out of earshot.

It was said that Nin was hard too, and maybe she was. She had raised a large family in those very lean times between the wars, and, perhaps, she had learnt to be hard, whatever 'hard' meant.

Nin had few clothes that I can recall: she appeared to wear only long pinnys with a cardigan underneath, together with a voluminous great-coat when she went out shopping, whatever the time of year. Her face was rounded, well lined and crinkled, and she hardly ever smiled; but we knew she loved us, her children and her grandchildren. Her love shone through the wrinkled features of her chubby face, however hard she tried to fight it back. She had the countenance of someone who had reared a family more by love than material things, through hard years, times when smiling was difficult or even meaningless.

Grandma Nin was a tiny lady who shouted constant threats of what would happen to us if 'You do that again!' Threats that never came to anything, because Mam said she shouted a lot just to make sure we all knew she was a very hard woman, someone to reckon with. Charlie and I loved her to pieces.

Nin and Grandad's living room, their backyard, and especially the shed, were sort of remote extensions to our house; whilst their thri'pence pocket money, every Saturday morning, doubled my income, though it had to be earned. That's where the bin-men came in.

Grandad had an allotment on the outskirts of Sevvy Park, and the neat mounds left by the bin-men's horses were his vegetables' main source of nourishment. It was my job to beat Jimmy Green in the race for the smoking piles of plant food, because Jimmy's Grandad had a plot next to my Grandad's. I usually beat him, because the bin collection started at our end of the street; but sometimes we ended up in battle over a particularly desirable mound. This often resulted in some of it in my wooden wheel-barrow but most of it over Jimmy and me. Triumphant, I would return home to be greeted by Mam:

'Sodden hell! You're forever covered in you know what, you are. I don't know what's up with you anyway, you must like it or something!'

Then I would be dragged indoors by the scruff of the neck, trailing little dollops of horse muck along the lobby.

What was left in the wheelbarrow was delivered to Grandad's backyard on Saturday mornings in return for my thri'pence pocket money: not a bad return for shovelling shit.

This then, was Liverpool 8 during and just after the war, when I was six or seven years old; a time when all the summers seemed long and hot and sunny; when the winters were short and it always snowed for us. Sometimes it rained too, but only the grown-ups seemed to mind.

Summer evenings were spent hiding from Mam as she tried to get us in for bed. 'Coo–ee! Kenneth; it's gerrin' late so gerrin' before I tell your dad!' It was the signal to hide with the others in the jigger until the sun's orange glow, dulled by the ever-present dust from the bombed sites, dipped behind the chimneys. Then we reluctantly meandered home, hands dug into our pockets, walking slowly to make the day as long as possible. And when we reached our doorsteps, the last of the day's insults were hurled; sure in the knowledge that they would be forgotten by morning.

Winters never had evenings, only short days and long nights, when the dust mixed with the smoke from thousands of coal fires, blackening your face by the time you were safely home from visiting Grandad.

To all but, perhaps, my immediate family, this chapter must have strained your patience, but I hope it has set the scene for the tales that follow.

Saturday Matinee

'Sixpence: a tanner – the sum needed to get in to the pictures.'

I am rich beyond the dreams of Avarice.
EDWARD MOORE

"OW MUCH 'AVE YOU GOT SPUD?'

Georgie was leaning on the windowsill and I was sitting on our front door step. I delved into my trouser pocket and extracted a thri-penny bit, four pennies and a ha'penny.

'Sevepence-ha'penny,' I announced, having checked the total three times. 'An' that's not counting the foreign ones.'

Uncle Charlie had given me some foreign coins last time he was home on leave from the army, and I was certain that one day they would be

Tunnel Road Picturedrome as it was in the 1970s
(courtesy Colin Wilkinson, www. streetsofliverpool.co.uk)

accepted as coins of the realm. So far, however, the local shopkeepers had shown a marked reluctance to accept Rupees.

'Ok,' said Georgie. 'You lend Terry a penny and we can all go.'
With some reluctance I handed over a penny. Georgie was being a bit too generous with my money.

'I 'aven't gorrenough.' Tommy's plaintive voice rose above our cheering.

Tommy always looked pale and under-nourished. He wore an open-necked shirt that was once white but was now yellowed by years of dolly-tubbing. The frayed collar, the absence of most of the buttons and the torn breast pocket, were evidence of it being his only shirt at that moment. Tommy's black tattered plimsolls looked enormous on the end of thin rickety legs, and his black pants with their shiny seat were not quite long enough to hide the legs of his shorts, which hung below his trousers showing them to be cut down pyjama bottoms.

Tommy had sparse, almost blond hair, which, because he was never told, was never washed – except when it rained – but the spiky clusters of his fair hair somehow matched the watery pale blue eyes and his frail body. His family was nearer to complete destitution than the rest of us, but he accepted his lot and took the inevitable insults without complaint, just being grateful he was one of the gang.

Secretly, we all liked Tommy and even felt a little sorry for him, because he really only had one problem as far as we were concerned, and that was not his fault. The problem was his baby brother Montgomery.

Montgomery was named after the Field Marshal of World War fame, because his father considered it essential to have a military name in the family, now that he had become a professional soldier. Tommy's dad had volunteered for the army; not waiting to be 'called up' like most of his friends, insisting that this made him a professional.

According to the women of the street he had volunteered about three days before he would have been called up anyway, and only did it because it gave him some say as to where he would be stationed. The fact that he got posted to northern Scotland for the duration of the war, just about as far away from the fighting you could get, gave some weight to the women's opinion.

Tommy's dad quickly rose to the rank of Lance Corporal: clear evidence of his being a professional soldier as far as he was concerned. According to the women, becoming a Lance Corporal was clear evidence of him being a creep, and a bit thick at that.

However, with full corporal only a matter of time and abject servility to his sergeant, it was enough for him to instruct the Vicar to christen his offspring with the same name as his war hero. It was a proud dad that heard the Vicar announce, 'I name this child Montgomery.'

His one regret was that he had relented to his wife's plea to drop the additional names he had planned. He would have loved to have a son called Field Marshal.

Montgomery was only three and could just about talk; though all he could say with clarity was 'Gimme gimme' whenever anything remotely resembling food came into sight; then, if he didn't get, he abandoned any further attempts at the spoken word, and bellowed.

It was normally Tommy's job to look after Montgomery, but today he was at home with his mother.

'Well it's 'ard luck then,' said Georgie. 'You never 'ave enough money anyway.'

We all stood up, except Tommy. He said nothing; there was nothing he could say. He just stared at the five pennies and a ha'penny neatly spread out between his legs, counting the coins again and again; trying to make them into sixpence, the sum needed to get into the cinema.

'Christ Almighty; it's me last ha'penny an' I wannit back by Monday!' I tossed the precious coin to Tommy. He watched the coin bounce towards him, hardly daring to believe his luck.

'Thanks Spud,' he said, quietly, without taking his eyes off the money. 'I'll make sure you gerrit back on Monday wivout fail,' he added, without much conviction. It had taken him three weeks to amass his five pence ha'penny.

In a moment of rare generosity I replied, 'You can 'ave it for keeps, so long as you don't bring bloody Gimme Gimme with you.'

Terry, Georgie, Tommy and I all now had sixpence, the magic sum needed to get into the Saturday Matinee at the Tunnel Road Picturedrome, a flea infested cinema known locally as the 'Tunny'.

It was only about half past eleven and the doors did not open until one o'clock, but we decided it was best to get there early to make sure we got in. It was a bit of a walk to the Tunny, so we set off right away. They were showing the last episode of 'Tarzan and the Lost City' and there was no way that we were going to miss that.

Terry led the way, running. We dodged through the jiggers between the streets, banging on the occasional back-yard door as we went. Georgie had been to last week's matinee and was describing in lurid detail how Tarzan had finished up. 'A croc'dile's gorrim and dragged 'im underwater; rippin' 'is guts out; and 'is monkey Cheetah's gorris knife an' won't go near the river; so I reckon 'e's 'ad it.'

'Bet he's OK,' I interrupted. 'He'll get the bloody knife somehow, an' there'll be nothing wrong with 'is guts. He always gets out somehow.'

I had noticed this before with Tarzan. The end of one episode showed him confronted with certain death, with no way out; but the beginning of the next episode was always slightly different. I could never figure it out. Why didn't he get into trouble in the middle of an episode so we could see how he got out of it? Whoever made the film obviously did not know what they were doing.

It was the same with Hopalong Cassidy. One minute he had been shot dead and fallen from his horse, tumbling head over heels down a ravine. Next minute he was standing up, gun blazing away and hat on head, with not a mark on him.

I liked the Three Stooges better; you knew where you were with them. The story started, had a middle and finished, all in one go.

'Buggeroff you lot!'

We had joined the end of the queue already forming in front of the Tunny, only to find Terry's older brother already there with his mates.

'Go on, 'op it!'

'You buggeroff. There's no law as says we can't stay 'ere is there?' Terry retorted.

Alan, Terry's brother, was four years older than Terry and a good deal bigger. Between them there was a sort of strange love-hate relationship: Terry loved Alan and Alan hated Terry.

Georgie and I edged away. You did not need the law on your side if you were bigger. As soon as we moved, a couple of enterprising kids from the next street jumped in front of us, separating us from Alan. This seemed to satisfy him and he turned back to his mates.

The queue gradually swelled and scuffles broke out as latecomers tried to sneak in. Some of the late arrivals were regulars who knew, to the inch, the position in the queue where you just got in before 'full house' was announced.

At long last and before too much blood had been spilled, the doors opened and a man in a once splendid uniform with fraying gold braid and a peaked hat appeared, intent on bringing some sort of order to the chattering crowd.

'Sixpenny stalls to the left, nine-penny balcony on the right!'

He disappeared under the stampede of cheering Tarzan fans. Some of the more crafty held back. They knew that if they timed it right, when the stalls were full but you had your sixpenny ticket, you would be allowed into the nine-penny balcony. In the general chaos, the really crafty ones got in for nothing. We never had the nerve to try and so we dutifully handed over our pennies then filed past the ticket box into the magical twilight of the vast cinema, clutching our tickets.

Usherettes greeted us as we entered the massive once-plush auditorium. They stood in a line like Roman soldiers, attempting to check the tickets, and ready to subdue the uncivilised hordes.

'You lot there; an' you lot over there, keep your feet off the seats. An' no chewin' gum!'

The usherettes directed their unruly customers with the military precision of Sergeant Majors. We obeyed without a murmur, fearful of the ultimate punishment of being thrown out without getting your sixpence back.

When all the seats were full, the usherettes picked out the smallest cinema-goers and they ended up two-in-a-seat. And when this method was stretched to the limit, anyone left was directed to sit on the floor in front of the first row of seats, with the great screen almost vertically overhead.

We managed to get one-in-a-seat about ten rows from the front, with the screen in full view except for the silhouettes of kids standing on their seat, and the occasional skirmish between those two-in-a-seat.

A few of the lights were not working but the splendour of the place was awesome. Acres of cream painted walls sprouted ornate gilded motifs. Great fluted pillars, decorated with cherubs and bunches of grapes, swept up to a massive vaulted ceiling as high as the sky; with an enormous brass chandelier hanging from the centre dome. It was a wonderful place.

If you were near the back or up-stairs in the gods, you could just make out the top of the organ, peeping over the pit in front of the voluminous folds of the dark green curtain. The organ was never played for Saturday Matinees, probably in the interests of the organ player; but my mother said it was always played on Saturday and Sunday nights, when any children in the audience had to be 'accompanied by an adult'.

Most of the audience were chattering or fighting, but some craned their heads backward and sideways to take in the splendour of the Tunny.

By coincidence Alan and his mates were only two rows in front of us.

After a few minutes, the audience became restless. They had paid their tanner and nothing was happening. Shouts of 'Gerron wiv it!' rose above the general chant of 'Why are we waiting? Oh why are we waitin'?' kept in strict time by the rhythmic stamping of hundreds of feet.

At long last the lights dimmed and the curtain rose slowly and majestically to reveal the great murky white screen.

A cheer exploded as the projector flickered into life.

An even louder groan exploded as it went off again.

'Purra bloody penny in the gas, it's gone out!' the audience screamed.

Renewed chanting of, 'Why are we waiting? Oh why are we waiting?' threatened the structure of the building.

Silence was temporarily restored by the sight of one urchin being frog-marched up the aisle, protesting loudly and tearfully that he '...never 'ad no apple, honest Missus, so 'ow could I 'ave chucked the core? An' I always eat the core anyway!'

The usherette was obviously not impressed. Someone had chucked an apple core and someone was going to be punished. The two someones did not necessarily have to be the same person.

Suddenly, the screen burst into life.

Next week's film trailers were the first offering; much appreciated by the audience. Optimistic plans were laid to definitely see most of what was on offer; plans well beyond the means of uncertain pocket monies.

Then came a cartoon; even more enthusiastically received, particularly as Popeye once again pulverised Bluto and sauntered into the setting sun, hand in hand with Olive Oil. No sooner had the happy couple disappeared into the sunset than the music rose to a crescendo to announce 'The Gaumont British News'.

Now Alan, Terry's brother, was not exactly good looking. A bit scrawny, even lanky, he had a small head with big round popping eyes. His most outstanding feature, however, was his enormous ears. Alan's ears were about half the length and width of his face and they stuck straight out sideways from his head. In celebration of this characteristic, we called him 'Old poppy-eyed-bat-ears' – though not to his face. Alan was very sensitive about his appearance, particularly the part played by his ears.

The screen showed the opening sequence of the Gaumont British News, with the newsreader intoning its famous introduction: 'The eyes and ears of the world'.

Normally the news was of little interest unless it showed our Armed Forces in action with pictures of dead German soldiers; but Terry was doubled up, pointing at the screen. He clutched his stomach with one hand and pointed at the opening credits of the Gaumont News with the other, spluttering in uncontrollable 'hee-hawing' laughter.

'Bloody eyes an' ears of the ... eyes an' sodden ears of the bloody world!' Terry collapsed again. He struggled to his feet, still overcome with laughter. 'Look, the sodden ...'

The fit of laughter got him again, but he managed to point at the screen then at something a few rows in front of us. 'Look, there they are, bloody eyes an' ears ... Look at our Alan: old poppy-eyed-bat-ears of the bloody world!'

He collapsed back in his seat.

A few kids took up the chant. 'Eyes an' ears of the world ... eyes an' ears of the world ...'

The chant grew, accompanied by the rhythmic stamping of feet. A few nearby chanters followed Terry's pointing finger, straight to Alan's ears.

'Eyes 'an ears of the world...' The chorus became more frenzied as the subject of their chant came into view. More and more joined in. 'Eyes an' ears of the world ... eyes and ears of the world ... eyes...'

Only Alan remained silent. He looked around to see what all the commotion was about, presenting a whole circle of his tormentors with the sight of his most outstanding feature. It slowly dawned on him that a hundred pointing chanters were pointing at him, and it slowly dawned on him what they were chanting. Someone in the gods worked out the words and soon the balcony had joined in.

Before long the whole cinema was throbbing to the stamping of feet and the chant. 'Eyes an' ears of the world ... eyes an' ears of the world...'

Everyone had joined in; everyone that is, except Alan and Terry.

Terry was now completely out of control, curled up in his seat, sobbing with laughter. Alan crouched down in his seat, trying to escape the torment, seething with impotent range and plotting the violent elimination of his sibling.

The audience kept it up until the projectionist, well used to anarchy at Saturday Matinees, changed over the reel half way through the news, to 'Episode Ten of Tarzan and the Lost City'. Silence gradually descended, helped by those who had been waiting all week for episode ten, thumping their still chanting neighbours.

''E never 'ad no bloody knife last week!' Georgie screamed, as the opening scene saw Tarzan set about stabbing a curiously floppy crocodile in a river about six inches deep.

I sat complacently back in my seat. 'Told you didn' I?'

Georgie was furious. He had looked forward all week to seeing Tarzan dismembered by the crocodile. 'Bloody swiz. 'Ow did 'e gerrit. Worr'I wanna know is, 'ow did 'e gerr'is knife!' He demanded, standing up to address the audience at large. 'Where did 'e gerris bloody knife from? 'Is sodden chimp 'ad it last week an' wouln't give it 'im, and now 'e's gorrit. 'Ow bloody come?'

'Shurrup you! And siddown or I'll sodden-well marmalise yer.'

Georgie swung round intent on doing battle, to be confronted by a great spotty-faced kid, about one and a half times Georgie's height and width, towering above him. A torn shirtsleeve and mud-stained tatty pullover testified to earlier battles.

''Oo the bloody 'ell do you think you're talking to?' Georgie blurted out the challenge before he had taken in the size of the problem. But then for once his brain worked fast. 'I was only sayin', last week 'e 'ad no knife, an' I wondered...'

Spotty-face shoved a big greasy hand into Georgie's face.

'Shurrup or I'll do yer!'

Georgie shut up; and I started a return to my seat from the end of the row where I had managed to scramble before Georgie shut up.

We settled down to watch the end of the film. Tarzan killed the croc-odile, Jane was kidnapped by some Arabs, then freed with the help of Tarzan's tame chimpanzee, Cheetah. Episode Ten ended with Cheetah running around with a gold idol from the Lost City, whilst the inhabitants laughed and cheered and thanked Tarzan for releasing them from their Arab slavers then saving them from the evil white treasure hunters.

The lights came on as Tarzan emitted ear-splitting yodels in answer to the bellowing herds of elephants that had helped capture the treasure robbers. All in all a very satisfactory end to the serial, as far as the audience was concerned, and they showed their appreciation by echoing Tarzan's earsplitting yodels.

The lights brightened and the screen announced an interval. Usherettes in neat pinafore uniforms materialised from the shadows and stood at the end of the aisles with a torch in one hand and a tray of ice creams slung from their necks. They were greeted with screams of approval and a chorus of wolf whistles from hundreds of scruffy kids.

Terry, ever optimistic, stood up.

"Ey Alan, give us some money for an ice cream.'

Alan was still in a state of shock, but the sound of Terry's voice stirred him into action. He jumped up and headed towards us, his ears silhouetted against the blank screen.

'Just you wait, you little sod!' he shouted.

Spotty-face saw him coming.

'Look, 'ere's the eyes and ears of the world comin'!' Spotty was on his feet, pointing at the approaching ears.

By this time Alan was only a few feet from Terry's throat; but he stopped in his tracks.

'You tryin' to be funny?' Alan turned on Spotty.

'No I wasn't, burrif I was, I'd gerran 'ead an' ears like yours. That'd make me bloody funny alright!' Spotty-face confronted Alan.

That was enough. The two sprang at each other, arms and legs flying.

The audience was delighted. Advice on the conduct of the fight came thick and fast.

'Put the boot in!' 'Gerr'old of 'is bloody great ears!' 'Kick 'is arse in!'

The sight of Alan in danger of having his arse kicked in overcame Terry's urge to live. Love of his older brother transcended all reason as he threw himself into the affray. Family honour was at stake. Spotty disappeared between the seats under the combined onslaught. After a few moments of grunting and swearing his head appeared from under the seat, to be

49

battered down again by Alan. It reappeared between Terry's knees. 'Barley, barley, I bags bein' barley!'

This universally accepted language of surrender worked. Terry stopped pummelling the spotty face and Alan, somewhat reluctantly, stopped kneeing him in the groin.

Everyone interlocked crooked little fingers as a gesture of forgiveness and everlasting friendship; just as the lights dimmed for the main feature film. The shouts and chattering died to an expectant silence as the cinema darkened. A few seconds later the Censor's 'X' Certificate flashed on the screen, to announce his verdict on the main feature, 'The Bride of Frankenstein.'

The screen slowly scrolled through the credits, but it was the music that commanded silence. The whole audience sat in rigid silence as threatening chords filled the auditorium to overwhelm the senses and set a scene of Gothic horror.

Tommy's pale face went white.

Then the tale of Frankenstein's hideous monster unfolded to the spine-chilling score: a horrifying tale of how second hand bits and pieces from dead criminals and a genius were all sewn together and brought back from the dead to make a hideous distortion of a man. A story of the determination of the monster to claim a bride whilst destroying all before it in the process, until it was itself destroyed in the inferno of Frankenstein's house: his house having been put to the torch by the bride's dad or somebody.

The wise amongst the audience, including Tommy, had shut their eyes at first sight of the monster and kept them shut until the screen went blank. Georgie, Terry and I watched it from beginning to horrible end.

Instead of the mad scramble to exit the cinema before 'God Save the King' was played, it was a subdued bunch that slowly filed out of the cinema to make our way home. Only Tommy acted normally. Even Alan was quiet and never objected when Terry sought comfort by taking hold of his hand.

Georgie made a half-hearted attempt to relive some of the events from Tarzan; but his efforts were lost to the memories of the monster's sewn-on head, with battery terminals sticking out of its neck.

It was nearly dark when we turned into our street. Normally we would have gone down the narrow and much darker jiggers; but not that evening. We walked on the edge of the pavement sticking close together in total silence, glancing behind in fearful anticipation of discovering a grotesque collection of body parts following us. Halfway home, a matinee-goer from the next street suddenly jumped out of a doorway declaring himself to be Frankenstein. His punishment was swift and harsh, once we had recovered from the shock.

So ended one of our rare visits to the Saturday Matinee at The Tunnel Road Picturedrome. It took three years before the memory of the monster's face faded enough for me to go to sleep without the lights on. Whoever mixed up the films and ended up showing The Bride of Frankenstein at a Matinee, had a lot to answer for: if nothing else, for the cost of three years of nightlights for the bedrooms of half the children in Liverpool 8.

Terry got away scot-free from insulting Alan's looks. He promised Alan that he would never ever call him old poppy-eyed-bat-ears ever again if he went to bed with him at the same time and left the light on for a while. Alan, with visions of the tortured monster still vivid in his mind, gratefully agreed.

Limping Johnny

'He stood there in the middle of the path in his navy-blue uniform,
exuding an air of menace: all four-foot ten of him.'

Power tends to corrupt and
absolute power corrupts absolutely.

LORD ACTON

'I'M-A TELLING YOU, I SAW ONE!' Terry was getting annoyed.

'Well I've never seen any and I've been there more times than you 'ave,' countered Georgie.

'Oh no you 'aven't,' said Terry.

'Oh yes I bloody 'ave,' retorted Georgie.

'Oh no you 'aven't,' insisted Terry.

Billy, with Tommy and I, sat on the edge of the pavement watching

Iron Bridge, Fairy Glen

Terry and Georgie performing their pantomime chant in the middle of the street, waiting for the verbal banter to move to physical assault.

'Oh yes I 'ave!' repeated Georgie.

It was just not good enough. They should be sorting out their differences with fists, not words.

I decided to speed up a resolution to the argument.

'He called you a liar,' I reminded Terry, helpfully. ''E said you hadn't seen one, an' he's calling you a liar. He said you didn't see a frog. I'd thump anyone who called me a liar, an' 'e called you a liar, didn't 'e?'

'Well I bloody well did see a frog; a big un. Who are you callin' a liar?' Terry launched himself at Georgie.

Billy, Tommy and I cheered the writhing grunting bodies on to greater effort.

Georgie began to get the upper hand.

'Punch 'im in the guts,' suggested Billy, Georgie's brother. Georgie could not oblige. Both hands were occupied gripping Terry's hair and pounding his head on the cobbles.

'Lerrim go or else!' Alan, Terry's older brother, was running along the pavement towards us.

Georgie let him go, much to our disgust. The fight was only just getting going and Georgie seldom got the upper hand; but when he did, he used it. It would have been interesting to see what effect longer term banging of Terry's head on the cobbles would have had.

Billy said it would make him gozzie, but I bet it would eventually kill him. Now we'd never know.

Peace was restored and Alan went on his way after clouting Georgie across the head to discourage further combat. Terry struggled to his feet and rubbed the back of his head.

'Look what you've bloody well done; me hair's full of tar.' Terry's fingers were covered by a black sticky mess.

'Anyway, I did see one, honest,' Terry insisted. 'It was in the middle of the pond wiv its head sticking out of the water; an' it was a big un, honest.' Terry's in-depth knowledge of a frog's habitat and demeanour convinced us.

'Well if there's one there's gorra be more,' said Tommy. 'So let's see if we can catch some.'

It was a Saturday morning and we had all been thrown out the house so that our mothers could get on with the housework. The sky was overcast but it was warm and dry, and we had been trying to decide what to do. Billy had suggested pulling down some of the remains of the walls on the bombed site at the end of the street, the 'debbie'; but this usually ended up with a brick-throwing raid and I was still suffering a cut leg from yesterday's battle. Tommy was against the idea too, though he stayed silent. Pulling down brick walls and bare feet did not mix too well. And Terry was not very enthusiastic either, thinking I might seek revenge on him for my cut leg.

It was at this point that Terry announced that he had seen a frog in 'Sevvy' Park.

We jostled along the gutter towards Lodge Lane, joining in Georgie's just invented lyric: 'We're goin' to Sevvy Park to catch a frog ... WE ARE going to Sevvy Park to gerra frog!' Sung to the only tune he knew: 'She'll be coming round the mountain when she comes!'

Crowds of women shoppers complaining about the prices white-washed on shop windows forced us to separate as we turned in to Lodgy. Billy spotted the horse-drawn bin wagon clopping down the middle of the road in the direction of Sefton Park. He broke into a run and caught up with it. The driver was on foot, leading the horse, and he and his mate were deep in conversation about something called a 'tanner each way'. They never noticed their passenger.

Billy was expert at hitching rides on the back of wagons and was clinging to the tail-board, oblivious to the anxious shouts of women to 'Gerroff before you kill your bloody self ... silly little sod!' The wagon clip-clopped unhurriedly towards the park, as Billy let go with one hand and waved at the anxious shoppers.

Suddenly, and without missing a single step, the horse did what comes naturally: depositing large steaming dollops at regular intervals along the road. At that very moment, the driver hauled on the reins as they reached their next stop.

The wagon juddered to a halt causing the stowaway to lose his grip. If it had not been for the forethought of the horse, Billy would have banged his head on the cobbled road. As it was, the large steaming dollops gently cushioned his face.

Billy struggled to his feet and sauntered over to us, wiping his face with the back of his hand and shaking half-digested sloppy globs of straw from his shirt and out of his trouser pockets.

'Bloody 'ell, you stink you do!' Tommy held his nose. 'Your mam will batter you.'

'It's not dirt is it,' Billy stated, 'it's not dirty, it's only 'orse-muck, it comes off, look.' He pulled a bit out of his buttoned fly. 'Look it comes off easy, an' it doesn't smell much.' There was nothing wrong with Billy's eyesight; most of it did come off; but his sense of smell was a bit suspect.

Billy led the way down Lodge Lane. For some reason or other the women politely moved out of his path, their faces contorted into a disgusted grimace as the stench drifted past.

PALM HOUSE, 'SEVVY' PARK

We ambled on, across Croxteth Road and down towards the Lodge at the gates to Sefton Park. The sight of the green fields signalled claims to be Robin Hood, Hopalong Cassidy and Gene Autry. When we had established who was going to be whom, we broke into a fast run, slapping our backsides and yelling 'gee-up!' at the top of our voices to urge imaginary mounts to greater efforts until at last we reined to a halt at the Needle monument, which stood at the top of a long tree-lined avenue leading down towards the heart of 'Sevvy'.

Being a Saturday, the avenue was thronged with mothers and grandmas and kids and dogs. New babies were being pushed in new prams; at least, those who came from Aigburth way were. Those from Lodgy way were pushed in prams that had carried their mams and grandmas down the same avenue, decades ago. Other tiny tots were carried as babes in arms, wrapped in mounds of suffocating shawls. The idea seemed to be to take new babies for walks in the fresh air without actually exposing them to it.

Tommy was lagging behind, when suddenly, he was accosted by a gang of scruffy urchins from Coltart Road. They were a bit older than Tommy.

'Where do yer fink you're goin?' A fat youth with a pudding basin haircut, long trousers and boots twice the size they should be, confronted Tommy. He was carrying his shirt in one hand and a small branch of a tree in the other.

'I'm wiv them,' said Tommy carefully, pointing down the avenue towards the rest of us. The gang from Coltart Road recognised us. We sometimes hurled bricks at each other on the debbies, and it was sort of generally understood that Coltart and our street were born enemies; though why, was lost in the mists of time.

Having spotted Tommy's plight, we were trying to decide whether to make a run for it or take on the challenge.

The fat youth poked Tommy with the stick and tried to stamp on his bare feet. 'What's up, can't you afford a pair a shoes or what?' Another blotchy faced youth joined in the taunting.

It was one thing for us to take it out on Tommy, that was our right; but for someone from Coltart Road to do it, that was just not on. Billy retraced his steps towards the gang, with the rest of us following, hoping something might happen to prevent the inevitable battle, because there were five or six in the gang and they were all bigger than us.

Even Billy hesitated when he got nearer. The gang clustered around the fat youth as we approached. We stopped a yard or two away, and the battle of trying to stare each other out began. After a few minutes it was obvious that nobody was winning the battle of the stares.

The fat youth approached Billy. 'Worra you gunna do about it then?' he demanded belligerently. Billy, who was a good six inches smaller than him, blanched. He had committed a major tactical error: instead of just sacrificing Tommy, he had sacrificed the lot of us.

'I just wondered...' Billy started, with an apologetic tone in his voice.

'Bloody 'ell you stink to buggery; worrav you done, shit yourself?' The fat youth held his nose between finger and thumb in an exaggerated gesture of disgust. Billy had decided to ignore our insults about his personal hygiene on Lodge Lane, but enough was enough. He sprang at his tormentor, arms and feet flaying, pummelling the fat youth's face with his fists, before setting about his shins with his boots.

The rest of the gang stood back in total shock. The sight of Billy in full fury was awesome.

The fat youth went down under the onslaught and Billy turned his attention to a gangling red-haired skinny boy who seemed to be made of nothing but arms and legs held together by an enormous bright blue jersey.

The arms and legs in the blue jersey soon went down. Without pausing, Billy looked for his next victim, but the remainder of the gang were halfway across the field, heading for home as fast as their legs would carry them.

'Aar-ee-aarh!' Georgie abandoned Gene Autry and announced he was Tarzan, pounding his chest and yelling a succession of triumphant 'Aar-ee-aarh's!' to warn off anyone else who might be thinking of taking us on.

In the meantime Tommy had picked up the fat youth's branch, the cause of a large red bruise on his foot, and was trying to push it down the youth's throat.

'Tell us you surrender!' Tommy demanded. 'Tell us or else!'

The fat youth stared up at the sky, his eyes wide with fright, any announcement of surrender being hindered by the end of the branch jamming his vocal cords. Tommy interpreted the agonised gurgling as words of abject apology and withdrew the stick. The youth staggered to his feet, spitting out bits of bark and leaves, then waddled off after his fast-disappearing friends, trailing his tatty shirt along the ground.

Near the end of the tree-lined avenue, just before it opened up to a wide paved area with its Eros statue and the Café, stood the grandly named Sefton Park Open Air Theatre: a green and cream painted wooden building, usually open on a Saturday afternoon.

The paying audience sat on wooden chairs on the lawn in front of the stage, whilst those who would not, or could not pay, thronged the railings surrounding the lawn.

We arrived just in time for the main feature of the afternoon, an amateur talent contest. The usual contestants were lined up at the side of the stage waiting their turn to enthral the audience, just as they did at every talent contest held there. Pretentious little girls in cute short frilly dresses showing dirty knickers, stood stiffly to attention whilst they mechanically intoned the first verse of their party-piece, then burst into tears as they forgot the second, just as they did last Saturday.

Others tap danced and fell over, to be dragged off sobbing by an impassive-looking compère, to be told how wonderful they had been, before being propelled into the arms of their anguished mothers.

'And now ladies an' genelmen, I give you the nightin-gale of Upper Parliament Street, Maggie O'Flannigan.' The compère intoned his introduction of the next act. A short fat lady in a dangerously low cut dress clutched hold of the microphone for support and with the business end half way down her throat sang 'The Lord is my Shepherd', 'Barefoot Days', 'It's a long way to Tipperary' and 'Nellie Dean', without pausing between songs and completely ignoring the pace set by the accompanying piano. She was eventually escorted off the stage for her own safety when she called for audience participation in 'Forty green bottles standing on the wall'.

The audience whistled and booed her departure, then broke into rapturous applause as another lady of uncertain age arrived on stage to do her impersonation of 'Our feathered friends from Sefton Park'. Having acknowledged her introduction with a gracious curtsey, she shoved two fingers between her lips and let forth with a series of ear-piercing whistles, frightening the life out of any feathered friends in the surrounding trees.

The contest was eventually won by unanimous vote for the last act: an elderly gentleman in an oversize grey overcoat and a cloth cap. He won for his somewhat slurred but otherwise faultless rendition of 'Eskimo Nell', the adult version. Most, though not all of the words were lost on the tap-dancers and his younger fans, but we all recognised talent when we saw it and joined in with the grown-ups' appreciation of this new star of Sefton Park's Open Air Theatre.

The elderly gentleman responded with the aplomb of a born enter-tainer and repeated verses three, six and thirteen, which summed up the whole story and the particular talents of Nell. After one last curtain call, he collected his prize – two tickets for the next week's Billy Smarts Circus – and left the stage to the accompaniment of the piano playing the grand finale: 'I've got a lovely bunch of coconuts.'

The crowd began to disperse. We followed them, with Billy telling us about the top-of-the-bill act he had seen at last week's show. He described, in lurid detail, the last act, which had been a man in a black suit and white shirt wearing a big shiny hat. The magician had set about sawing a woman in half as she lay trapped in a long box with her head sticking out one end and her feet out of the other.

This kind of entertainment was right up Billy's street. He described the dying screams of the woman and the ensuing torrents of blood that accom-panied the entertainment. 'Right in bloody 'alf she was ... guts all over the place.' Nobody was sure just how much to believe him. Certainly there had been such a show. My brother Charlie had seen it. But Charlie had not mentioned the guts or even the blood. If there had been any mutila-tion, I was sure Charlie would have mentioned it, because Billy and Charlie shared the same sort of thinking as far as pain and suffering of others was concerned.

'Carted off the bits in a sack, bloody smashin' it was,' Billy concluded.

The excitement over, we ran on down towards the Eros fountain to carry out the routine search for coins that someone said were thrown into foun-tains by adults, for luck. As usual there was nothing in it but leaves. Once again we were disappointed but not surprised. Adults had all the luck they needed anyway, without having to pay for it.

Terry sauntered over towards the café, up the terrace steps, and peered through the open door. 'Cor, look at that lot!' Terry shouted back at us. We dashed up the steps to join him. The counter in the café was bedecked with jars of sweets and bottles of pop.

'Don't suppose anyone's gorrany money 'ave they?' Terry asked. There was no answer.

A couple of girls in bright flowered dresses and ribbons in their hair, skipped past us hand in hand, and tilted their heads to look down their noses at the grubby faces leering at their ice creams.

'Gis a suck.' Terry shouted as they headed for the steps. He instantly regretted the request. Terry had not seen their Nanny, a few steps behind them.

Terry nursed the back of his head. 'Christ Almighty!' he groaned, 'I only asked for a suck. Think I was gonna pinch their rotten ice cream off 'em. Chris' Almighty, she nearly knocked me bloody 'ead off!'

There was no point in torturing our taste buds anymore, so we followed the Nanny down the steps at a healthy distance. The wide path led past Eros and alongside one of the lakes. The lake had a beautifully kept island with ornamental shrubs and great oak and horse chestnut trees. In the middle of the island stood a fine bandstand with ornate gold-topped railings and intricate iron arches.

The bands only played on Sundays, so we paused just long enough to go through the ritual of searching the grass where the audience sat, for lost coins.

'I'm tellin' you,' stated Terry, 'I found thri'pence once. It must 'ave fell out of someone's trouser pocket when they watched the band. Stands to reason, when you sit down the money rolls out of your pockets.' Just how Terry worked this out, we were not sure. Terry never had any money to roll out; and he had holes in his pockets anyway.

Either Terry was wrong or the audience had been flat broke like us; because we found nothing.

We ambled on in a straggling line along the path, with Tommy rattling his branch on the railings.

'Canada goose that one,' stated Billy, pointing to a small flock of wildfowl circling the lake then landing for scraps of bread thrown by the little girls with the ice creams.

Georgie stared at the flock. 'Which one?' he demanded, 'and how come it's a Canada one?'

Billy pointed out the largest of the birds with a black head and brown body. 'That one there; the big 'un; the one that's trying to kill that mallard.'

We all stared at him, wondering at his in-depth knowledge of wildfowl. My knowledge was somewhat limited: any birds not on water were sparrows of different colours; and anything on water was a duck.

In the middle of the island stood a fine bandstand with ornate gold-topped railings and intricate iron arches

'It comes from Canada by miggitting,' said Billy. 'Every year it miggits and the mallards doesn't.'

The little girls' Nanny had overheard Billy's explanation. Determined to build on any sign of civilised behaviour shown by the lower classes, she said, 'That's right, young man; it comes all the way from the snowy wastelands of Canada. Just think, it migrates every year over all those thousands of miles just to come to Sefton Park.'

Terry kept his distance, but the rest of us gathered around Billy. It was not often adults took much notice of anything we said, and this was a posh adult.

'And you are quite right too,' she continued. 'That is a mallard drake and he usually stays here all the year round.' We listened spellbound, though only just able to understand her King's English. The Nanny turned to her charges. 'Now wasn't it clever of this little boy to know where the wildfowl come from?' The two spick and span little girls said nothing. They studied us one by one, head to foot, with obvious distaste.

Nanny stuck to her new role of encouraging refinement in ruffians. 'Now tell me young man, how do you know so much about the ducks and geese?'

Billy hurriedly retracted the tongue that was pointing at the little girls and looked up at the Nanny.

'Now come on young man, don't be shy, tell everybody how you know.'

Billy finally plucked up courage to answer. 'Me Grandad told me Miss.' He called any woman who was not an aunt, 'Miss', because the only ones who spoke to him who weren't aunts, were school-teachers. His ruddy freckled face flushed with pride as he expounded his knowledge. 'Me Grandad told me, when 'e got one from the park keeper for Christmas dinner, Miss. And when 'e gorrit 'ome 'e said it was a duck; and when 'e pulled its guts out and shoved stuffin' up its arse to gerrit ready for me Mam, 'e said it was a mallard.'

The little girls' Nanny went white but the little girls looked at Billy with new interest.

Billy, still full of pride at his new status as a wildlife expert, continued at full speed. 'An' Grandad gorranother bigger one wiv it; one of them ones.' He pointed to the geese amongst the flock. 'An' when 'e gorrit ready for the oven 'e said it was a goose; and 'e said fancy miggitting all the way from Canada to get your bloody head chopped off an' bread-crumbs shoved up your arse.'

We reached the far end of the lake. Billy was still rubbing his cheek.

'What she do that for? What she go an' 'it me for?' he demanded, for the umpteenth time. 'I only told her what she asked, didn' I? What she do that for?'

Nobody could enlighten him; it was a complete mystery.

The main path continued on and downhill to eventually circle the big boating lake; but first it divided the smaller lakes, breaking into stepping stones as it met the stream connecting the lakes. A narrow path branched off to the left, leading the way to the Fairy Glen.

Billy reckoned he could get across the stepping stones with three jumps.

Georgie bet him he wouldn't make it.

The bet was won by Georgie. Billy got wet and thumped Georgie by the way of payment.

Georgie didn't seem to mind; he always got thumped when he was right and Billy was wrong; but no amount of thumping could change the fact that he was dry and Billy was wet.

Terry reckoned he could walk across with his eyes shut.

I bet him he couldn't. I won and he got wet.

Tommy got wet too. He simply waded in, zig-zagging between the stones backward and forward.

I threw my pumps over the far side and jumped in with Tommy.

That left Georgie as the only one with dry feet and he jumped in to save Billy the trouble of throwing him in.

Soaking wet, but exhilarated, we squelched up the steps at the end of the stepping stones and up the grassy slopes to the beginning of the Fairy Glen.

The Glen was a miniature valley of exotic shrubs and trees, carefully planted either side of a small stream that made its way down eventually to the boat lake. The way in was barred by arrowhead railings and a gate with a notice announcing that the Fairy Glen was 'Open from 9.00am to 6.00pm. Dogs must be led on a lead. Children not allowed unless accompanied by an adult.'

Extreme caution was needed if we were going to avoid the Cocky-Watchman, who ensured strict adherence to the rules, from his seat on a park bench just beyond the gate.

I decided the best thing to do was to become Robin Hood and his band of outlaws, the Merry Men. They were skilled at moving unnoticed in the green woods. Billy, the biggest of us, bagged Little John and I was Robin Hood. Terry, who happened to be wearing the remains of a bright red pullover stuck to historical accuracy and said he would be Will Scarlet. Georgie, somewhat reluctantly, decided on Friar Tuck and Tommy resigned himself to being an unnamed outlaw.

''Ow do we gerrin, Spud?' demanded Friar Tuck.

'Down 'ere, along the edge of the river; an' its Robin bloody Hood, not Spud.'

I glared at the Merry Men, then led the way down the newly mown grass slope towards the stream and into a canopy of rhododendrons.

It was like entering another world.

Underfoot was a soft and crunchy rich brown compost of decades of fallen leaves and twigs. Overhead, the screen of leaves and branches filtered the sunlight to produce an eerie gloom; just like the Sherwood Forest of our imagination.

I led the Merry Men on through the gloom, forcing our way through the tangle of branches. We kept in contact with hoarse whispers.

'Aye! Look at them.' Terry forgot he was an outlaw.

He was hanging on to a rhododendron branch, leaning full stretch over the stream, and pointing with his free hand into its murky depths. We scrambled to get to him to see what he was pointing at.

In his haste, Friar Tuck stumbled and grabbed Will Scarlet's pullover to save himself from falling. Rhododendrons are not the strongest of bushes and whilst this one was up to the weight of one outlaw, the combined weight of Scarlet and Tuck was too much for it. In they went.

Somehow or other they managed to stay on their feet, swaying back and forward trying desperately to remain upright, knee-deep in the muddy water and facing each other.

'What did you do that for? Bloomin' idiot!' Will Scarlet maintained his hoarse whisper, even though their descent into the mud had the birds for miles around squawking in terror.

'Couldn't help it,' whispered Georgie. 'I tripped over a root or some-thing. Anyway what were you looking at?' He kept to his hoarse whispering despite the rest of the Merry Men rolling about in the bushes howling with laughter.

'It's full of tiddlers,' Terry answered, leaning over to talk softly into Georgie's ear. ''Undreds of them.' They both proceeded to walk slowly down the middle of the stream, searching the water for signs of its popula-tion of sticklebacks. 'Frogs eat 'em, so there must be frogs around 'ere all right,' Terry continued to talk straight into Georgie's ear. Georgie, whose knowledge of the eating habits of frogs was about as good as his fellow outlaws', agreed with him.

'Gerrout of the water before someone hears us. Forget about the tiddlers, we've come about frogs,' I insisted. They joined the rest of us and squelched their way through the undergrowth.

'Shurrup you two!' Billy glared over his shoulder. ''Ow do you expect to gerrin if you're makin' noises like a bloody whale?'

The two wet outlaws changed to an exaggerated tiptoeing, moving more slowly, but just as loudly. The bushes began to thin out and we could see the unlocked gate to the Fairy Glen about twenty paces away.

'Get down!' I whispered. The Merry Men lay down in a line, peering under the branches across the open ground to the gate. 'You go and we'll give you cover.' I nudged Tommy. I was not quite sure what 'cover' meant, but the cowboys in films did it, and it seemed to work.

Tommy hesitated. 'Worrappens if I get nicked?' he demanded, without taking his eyes off the gate. 'They'll shove me in jail … they might 'ang me.' I was not too sure what would happen if he got caught, but capital punish-ment seemed a bit harsh.

'Don't be stupid,' Billy whispered, 'they'll probably only belt yer one!'

Tommy contemplated this piece of good news. 'Well if that's all they'll do, why don't you go? You're Robin Hood not me.' Tommy looked straight at me.

I weighed up the idea of getting belted against the job of gang leader.

Four pairs of eyes studied me expectantly.

I assumed the air of a born leader.

''S no problem to me.' I managed to choke out the reply.

'Well go on then,' Billy insisted. 'What are you waitin' for?'

'I'm waitin' for you to cover me,' I answered, praying something would happen to save me.

'We are covering you!' the outlaws chorused.

'Go on then!' Billy gave me a helpful shove.

'You lot sure you're covering me?' I half got to my feet.

'Course we are; gerron wiv it,' Tommy insisted.

I stood up and peered left and right. There was nobody in sight. Bent double, I dashed across the open space to the gate, pulled up the latch and shoved. The gate was stuck.

Panic gripped me as I heaved at the gate, rattling it back and forward, fighting the urge to flee.

The gate remained firmly wedged.

'It's stuck,' I shouted back to the Merry Men, my voice pitched high with panic.

'Give it a bloody good shove,' Terry advised, from the safety of the rhododendrons.

I gave the gate an almighty shove.

It swung open with me still clinging to it, hurling me in an arc, through the opening. The gate crashed to a halt against a rock, but I kept going and ended up in a holly bush. The sound of muffled laughter floated across the open space. I ignored them. I was in the Glen and there was still no sign of authority.

'You lot still covering me?' I shouted back over my shoulder.

Guffaws of laughter answered me. 'Done all right so far 'aven't we?' said Terry.

So far nobody had belted me or attempted to throw me into jail, so I supposed he must be right. I slunk, half-crouched, along the shrub-lined path by the side of the stream.

Though it was lost on me at the time, the Glen really was a lovely pretty place. The stream ran from private property on the far side of the perimeter road of the park, under the blue painted cast-iron bridge that carried the road at tree top height, then twisted and turned through the Glen before making its way to the Boat Lake.

Tiny rolling lawns, the flowering shrubs and carefully planted beds of roses, the clumps of taller trees; they all blended under the frame of the blue painted bridge to form a lovely tranquil place.

I tiptoed up a path, with each twist and turn revealing a different design of tiny water garden. The path ahead curved under the bowed branch of a splendid oak and then, there it was! I glimpsed a small lily-covered pond: the home of our frogs!

The pond was fringed on one side by the path and it overflowed between stepping stones, across the path, to join the main stream. It was fed by a spout of water cascading down an almost sheer rockery on the far side, covered in hanging plants and ferns. The path made its way past the pond and eventually to the top of the rockery and thence to the cast-iron bridge.

It was a lovely secret place.

I continued to skulk along the path, the prettiness of my surroundings dulled by the thought that authority might be lurking amongst all these bloody bushes. The way ahead, however, seemed clear enough and I had made it as far as the overhanging oak. There was no sign at all of a park keeper and the pond was only a few yards further on.

Curiosity had replaced laughter amongst the rest of the outlaws and I could hear them stealthily crunching along the path some distance behind me. In another second or two the Fairy Glen's pond would be ours to search for that rarest of creatures: the near extinct Liverpudlian Frog.

Suddenly I heard the sound of breaking twigs behind me. I whirled around in horror. One moment we were alone in the glen, the next he was there!

He had appeared from nowhere; standing between me and my faithful followers. Authority had arrived as if by magic to protect the Glen against children not accompanied by adults; and it appeared in the form of a uniformed parky! He stood there in the middle of the path in his navy blue uniform, exuding an air of menace: all four foot ten of him.

The parky was only a couple of inches bigger than me, but his flat peaked cap was made for the full grown version. Rather than just being worn, the cap appeared to envelop his head. His eyes peered out from the narrow slit between the rim of the hat and the collar of his enormous overcoat.

Horror at the sudden appearance of authority turned to abject terror as I saw he had no hands. Then I realised he did have them, but they were hidden by the length of his sleeves. His feet were also missing; but I supposed they were somewhere in the concertina-like folds of his trousers, dragging along the ground.

'Come 'ere you, you little sod!' The deep voice sounded much too big for its owner.

I was at the in-between stage in reading: struggling with the long words in Enid Blyton's *Famous Five* adventures, having just mastered the last of her literary works on *Noddy in* Toytown. There was no doubt about it, Noddy's friend, Mr Plod the policeman, was based on fact – the evidence was right in front of me.

The parky suddenly realised I was not alone and swung his head round to see who was following me. Plod's head pivoted under his oversize hat, but the hat stayed put, its peak still pointing at me.

The outlaws were in full flight, so he quickly turned back to me, catching up with his hat. 'Come 'ere you, you little git!'

Noddy's friends didn't use language like that, so he wasn't the nice Mr Plod I'd read about, after all.

I backed away from him.

He limped after me.

I backed away a few more yards.

The parky limped after me.

After retreating about twenty yards it dawned on me that there was no way he was going to get me at the rate of progress he was making. The wicked streak in every child came out as I backed away again, more slowly, just to make sure I was right.

Sure enough, he limped even more slowly after me.

Flushed with power, I forgot any finer points of behaviour that my mother had tried to instil and slowed down the retreat yet more, keeping just out of reach.

I shouted back at the fast disappearing outlaws. 'It's alright,' I yelled. 'You can come in; 'e limps!' There was no response. They must have reasoned that I had been caught and was trying to reduce the prison sentence by shopping them.

By this time I had mentally re-christened Mr Plod, 'Limping Johnny'.

I yelled again. 'I told you, it's alright; 'e's 'ere but 'e can't get you because 'e limps.' Four tousled heads peered cautiously through the bushes, still a little distance away. 'You can come in, Limping Johnny won't mind,' I advised them, full of arrogance, in the sure knowledge that I could out-run authority with no trouble at all.

The park keeper had stopped following. Suddenly, he appeared to become afflicted with a twitch: he kept glancing up at the sky then back to me. His hat never moved as he tilted his head up and down, causing his eyes to disappear under the rim and reappear in time with his twitch.

The Merry Men stayed at a safe distance.

My position as their gang leader was assured forever, as I showed them my complete mastery of the situation by keeping my eyes on the parky and taking one step towards him then two away. Limping Johnny faltered after me. One step forward, two steps back; I retreated up the path towards the steps leading to the bridge, drunk with power. Limping Johnny's twitch seemed to be getting worse. His eyes appeared then disappeared in rapid succession as he glanced up at the sky then back to me.

One step forward; two steps back …

A shadow descended on the path and a great hand descended on my head. 'Smart-arse, ay!'

I almost fainted with fright.

The hand gripped me round the head and twisted me around. I found myself staring at shiny silver buttons embossed with the crest of the Liverpool City Constabulary. Real authority had arrived of the fully-grown variety. In fact, overgrown.

The policeman towered above me, his six-foot-something height becoming seven foot to the top of his bobby's helmet. Unlike Limping Johnny, the helmet perched precariously on top of an oversize round head. This was the real Mr Plod.

If he had not been gripping my head like a cricket ball, I would have passed out.

'What's 'e been doin'?' the giant Mr Plod asked Limping Johnny.

'Nothing yet,' the parky replied. 'He didn't have time; I got him first ... except he's being hard-faced.'

The giant transferred his grip from my head to an ear. ''Ard-faced ay; well we'll have to do something about that then, won't we? Anyway, what are you doing in 'ere; can't you read or something?'

I thought quickly. It came to me in a flash. If I could not read, I could not be blamed for taking no notice of the sign on the gate!

'No, Sir,' I replied faintly.

'How old are you then?' Limping Johnny asked, with maybe a tinge of sympathy in his voice.

'Eight and a half,' I replied. 'Eight last May.' I added a couple of years for effect.

'Eight and you still can't read, eh? What school do you go to?'

'Tiber Street,' I replied uneasily. The conversation was taking a distinctly dangerous turn.

'In that case I'll have a word with Mrs Bell, the headmistress; I know her very well,' continued Limping Johnny, looking me straight in the eye. 'What's your name?'

The dialogue had gone dreadfully wrong. I looked around for inspiration from the rest of my faithful followers, but there was no sign of them; they were rounding the corner of Lodge Lane, still running hard.

'Well come on; what's your name?'

There was no way out, I had to own up.

'Billy ...' I replied.

Next Monday Billy was summoned to the Headmistress.

He got one stroke of the cane for being hard-faced and cheeky with authority, another one for pulling down the reputation of Tiber Street County School, Junior Mixed, and a third for lying about his reading ability.

Later in the day Billy was complaining bitterly. 'How come it was you as was caught, but it was me who got the bloody cane? How come? That's what I wanna know.'

It was a mystery to me too, I assured him.

The adventure brought a lot of respect for Limping Johnny, despite his infirmity and the difference in size between him and his uniform. Anyone who could summon a giant Mr Plod by glancing up at the sky, commanded respect, particularly if they knew our headmistress.

Terry and I decided to have another go at finding frogs a few weeks later; but this time without the rest of the outlaws. We got as far as the rhododendron bushes opposite the gate.

'I'll give you cover 'an you gerrin first, Spud,' Terry whispered.

'You can sod off,' I replied. 'I did it last time, so it's your turn.'

We spent five minutes arguing in hoarse whispers, finally agreeing that we would go together. There was no sign of Limping Johnny nor, more to the point, the giant Mr Plod. We crept along the path towards the pond. There was still no sign of authority.

Just off the path however, and unseen by Terry and I, a pair of smiling eyes surveyed us from under the rim of an enormous park keeper's hat.

'You keep watch Spud, an' I'll 'ave a look for frogs.'

Terry crawled to the edge of the pond and started to search the weed-covered surface. There was no sign of life, except sticklebacks and insects.

'Bloody thing must 'ave moved.' Terry whispered.

'It could only 'ave moved if there was one 'ere in the first place.' I muttered.

Terry turned to me. 'Are you calling me a liar or something?' he said, the light of battle dawning in his eyes. ''Cause if you are...'

It was not the time or place to start a punch-up.

'I'm not saying you are a liar, exactly,' I replied, 'only you might 'ave mistaken a leaf for one, or something.'

Terry assumed this to be an apology and continued his search. 'It must be hiding or gone somewhere else; we'll have to come back later and 'ave another look.'

We tiptoed back down the path and out of the gate to safety. No sooner had we gained neutral territory than Limping Johnny appeared out of the bushes. 'Oh, it's you again is it?' his eyes peered through the slit between his cap and collar.

We froze on the spot, praying that he would not glance up at the sky again and summon the giant policeman. He didn't, he kept his eyes on us, but I looked up just to make sure that there was no sign of Plod's hand descending.

'I hope you haven't been in the Glen again ... you haven't, have you?' There was a twinkle in the park keeper's eye, unnoticed by us.

I hesitated; wondering whether to own up, tell a lie, or advise him that Terry had but I hadn't, by way of a middle course.

'We was only lookin' for frogs, Sir, honest to God; 'cause 'e said there was frogs in the pond and I'd like to 'ave a look at one, but there wasn't any, so 'e must 'ave been lying.' I looked accusingly at Terry. "An I wouldn't 'ave come if it hadn't been for 'im.'

Terry prepared himself for flight. It might be all his fault, but he wasn't prepared to go to the scaffold for it.

'Well, did you find any?' Limping Johnny asked. 'Because if you do, you mustn't take them home, they will only die, and that's not fair is it?'

We could hardly believe our ears. He seemed to be interested. There was no sign of a threat in his voice; no sign that he was about to summon the giant Plod. He was actually talking to us and not even hinting at reporting us to Mrs Bell.

Terry paused. Maybe there was a way of gaining a stay of execution. 'No, we didn't find any, Sir, honest,' replied Terry. 'And we wouldn't take 'em away even if we found one. But there is some in there isn't there? Because I saw one a few weeks ago; and the others said I was a liar, and...' Terry's face went pale as he realised he had admitted to an earlier crime.

'Few weeks ago, eh ... so you've been in here before have you? You must like the place.' Terry said nothing; he had said more than enough already.

If Tommy was right and you could be hung for ignoring the notice on the gate, then he'd be sentenced to death, twice. Terry's face drained of all colour. What on earth would his mam say if he was strung up before his seventh birthday?

'Was the one you saw a Common Frog or a Green Frog?' Limping Johnny continued, 'because there's plenty of Common Frogs around, if you know where to look; but I've never seen a Green one in the Glen.'

I thought hard. The frogs I had seen in Woolton were sort of half green and half brown, but I reasoned that any frog seen in Liverpool must be common. In fact my mother reckoned that most things in Liverpool were common. She was forever telling me not to play with so and so because ''E's as common as muck 'e is.'

'A common one,' I answered, ''e must 'ave seen a common one, mustn't you?' I turned to Terry. Terry nodded his head in agreement.

The park keeper limped through the gate towards us. Terry hurriedly backed away. 'It's alright, I'm not going to report you or anything; and if you promise faithfully you won't harm them or take any away, I might show you some frogs.' It was unbelievable. Far from having us arrested and thrown into jail pending execution, he was inviting us into forbidden adult-land. 'Well come on then, if you want to. It makes a change to find kids interested in things instead of nicking them. Now if you really promise not to harm them, you can come and have a look.'

'We won't harm them, Mister, honest!' Terry and I chorused. 'Cross me 'eart and 'ope to die.'

Our sacred promise convinced him. 'Ok then, follow me. By the way, what's your names? ... and no fibbing.'

'I'm Terry, and 'e's Spud 'ayter' Terry answered, almost dancing with excitement.

'That's funny,' said Limping Johnny, 'I thought your name was Billy.' The park keeper turned to me with a smile, then set off along the path, beckoning us to follow. We followed close on his heels as he dipped his way along the path. At least we followed his crumpled uniform. From the back there was no evidence that the uniform was occupied, there wasn't even a slit between hat and collar like there was on the front.

Along the path, past the pond where Terry claimed he had seen a frog, we made our way towards the cast-iron bridge. Then he turned off the path and threaded his way carefully between bushes and flower beds, to follow the stream, until the bridge loomed over us.

Little sunlight filtered through the trees and under the bridge. Here the air was dank and heavy with the smell of fungus and decaying leaves. The ornamental shrubs and close-cropped lawns of the Glen had given way to leafy mulch, dotted with wild elder and hawthorn bushes. Further along the stream you could just make out the edge of a garden running down to the water's edge.

Limping Johnny shuffled on towards the garden until we came to a fence. By this time we had left the cover of the bridge, and sunlight reappeared, glinting through enormous beech trees. He beckoned us to stop, and put his finger to his mouth, telling us to be quiet. Then he pointed to a half-hidden pond, fed by the stream.

It was a mysterious and secret place, that little pond surrounded by towering trees with their roots its bank and its surface carpeted by dense green floating weed.

The three of us stood together searching every inch of the carpet. After a couple of minutes without seeing a living thing, the park keeper pointed to a small clump of reeds just to our left.

There, peeping through the weed, were two of that most secret and rarest of all creatures: the Liverpudlian Frog.

That was the first of many a visit to our secret pond.

We kept our promise to leave the frogs in peace. And just to make sure they came to no harm, we never told our secret to a single living soul.

As often as not Limping Johnny would join us as we sat on a fallen log and watched, entranced, as the frogs went about their business.

We always sought his permission before entering the Glen and he always gave it. When we had finished frog watching, Limping Johnny would sit us down on his bench just inside the gate and enthral us with stories of the creatures that inhabited the Fairy Glen and the fields and lakes of Sefton Park. He told us where water voles could be seen and how he had once seen a big pike in the Boat Lake take a baby mallard. He told us about birds that were not sparrows, and of ducks that were gulls and swans and even herons.

Terry had been ill for a couple of weeks and we had missed our visits to Sevvy.

At long last he was well enough to go out, and his mother, offering thanks to the Good Lord, gave him thri'pence and sent him out to play. Later that day we set off for the Glen, wondering what tales our new friend would have in store for us. We ran all the way from the café and arrived breathless at the Fairy Glen.

There was no sign of Limping Johnny.

The air was still that day, heavy with scent of mown grass: too quiet a place for us to disturb. And so we never spoke; we sat on the grass and studied the stream in silence, waiting for Limping Johnny to arrive and take us to see our frogs.

A shadow spread across the grass. We looked up, delighted.

A park keeper stood there, towering above us. But it wasn't our friend. This one had hands and a face, and a smart new uniform with a cap that fitted.

'What are you two doing in here?' he demanded, 'you're not supposed to be in the Glen unless accompanied by an adult!'

Terry and I looked at each other, wondering why he was here and not our Limping Johnny. Terry answered him. 'We can come in by ourselves, Sir. The other one lets us in so long as we leave the frogs alone. We came to look for the other parky, Mister, the one as limps; an' then we were goin' to 'ave a look at the frogs wiv 'im.' Terry returned to studying the stream.

The park keeper sat down on the grass in front of us. 'Are your names Terry and Spud?' he asked, gently.

'Yes Mister,' Terry answered, 'an' the other parky as limps knows us an' we come to see 'im, honest. 'E tells us all about the animals and birds and things an' I saw a bloody big seagull wiv a black 'ead an' Limping ... I mean the parky as limps would know worrit's called.'

The park keeper surveyed us quietly for a few minutes. 'Yes, I'm sure he would know what it's called.' He paused for a moment as if undecided what to say. 'He told me he had two young friends who came to see him.'

He hesitated again. Terry and I swelled with pride at being told we were Limping Johnny's friends. 'He told me to let you know that so long as you ask the park keeper first, you can always go and see your frogs.'

'We always do, Sir,' I said. 'We tried to find 'im before an' we was only goin' to go under the bridge because we thought 'e might be there.'

'That's all right, I understand.' The park keeper looked around the Glen as if trying to avoid our eyes. 'But in future you'll have to see me.'

'Worrabout Limping Johnny? Worrabout the one as limps? 'E's the one as knows everything; and 'e likes us an' we like 'im, Mister. Why can't 'e be 'ere?' We stared wide-eyed at the Keeper.

'Limping ... Mr Moores was getting on a bit you know, young fellows, and he's not been very well lately; and ... well ... well never you mind, you come and see your frogs whenever you want to.'

For some reason or other, it didn't seem right to go to our pond that day, and we left the Glen in silence.

Terry and I returned home with a strange feeling in our stomachs, a feeling that we never experienced again until much later in life. We never saw Limping Johnny again.

Some weeks later Terry and I went back to the pond for the last time. We sat together on a log at the edge of our secret pond and thought about Limping Johnny.

We recalled the first time he summoned the giant Mr Plod. We thought about his tales of the animals that lived in his Glen, and we pictured in our minds, his kindly eyes peeping between the peak of his cap and the collar of his oversized uniform.

There was no sign of life in the pond that day, but we knew there was some presence in that quiet place.

Terry and I left the pond in silence.

We both knew we would never see Limping Johnny again, but our Liverpudlian frogs were still there, somewhere, and we had that strange feeling sometimes experienced in special places: that someone unseen was with us, someone who shared the love of that place.

Tiber Street Mixed School

'Within the fabric of the building there must remain the echoes of its past: the chanting of a thousand times tables, the laughter of children at play in the school yard, and perhaps some tears. 'Minutes later, the heavy green gate was shut with an echoing clang. The chattering died to hushed whispers.'

Abandon every hope, ye who enter here.

Divine Comedy, Dante Alighieri.

TIBER STREET SCHOOL

Within the fabric of the building there must remain the echoes of its past: the chanting of a thousand times tables, the laughter of children at play in the schoolyard, and perhaps some tears

IT WAS A SUNNY LATE SUMMER MORNING a few months after my fourth birthday, and I was playing Jinks outside our house with Terry.

Terry stood in the gutter and took his throw. It was a good one: his bright-red Walker's Ale bottle-top landed hard against the doorstep. There was no way I could beat that, so I adopted diversionary tactics.

'What the 'ell do they wanner go in there for?' I pretended to forget it was my turn to throw, and sat down on the edge of the pavement with my feet in the gutter. Terry joined me.

We stared at the small groups of boys and girls, all a bit older than us, trudging along the street, then through the gate opposite, into the yard of Tiber Street School; some chattering, but most in silence.

Minutes later, the heavy green gate was shut with an echoing clang. The chattering died to hushed whispers. We continued to watch as the children lined up in straight rows, before being marched into the dark recesses of the school, through a massive door labelled 'Infants'.

'Me mam says we'll 'ave to go to school one day.' Terry started to pick the tar from between the cobbles.

'You can go if you want, burr-I'm not sodden-well goin'!' I retorted.

Charlie, my older brother, went to the 'Seniors' but I had advised my mother that, whilst it was probably a good thing for Charlie, I wouldn't have the time to go. It was difficult enough as it is, finding the time to play out as well as getting enough sleep; so that was the end of the matter as far as I was concerned. If Terry's mam wanted him to go, that was his problem; there was no way I was going.

Terry continued to stare at the school gate, absentmindedly rolling the tar into a ball between the palms of his hands. 'Well you can go, but I'm not,' I repeated, interrupting his thoughts. 'Christ, they only let you out for a couple of minutes. They ring a bell an' call it playtime. 'Ow the sodden 'ell can you play proper when they keep the gates locked?'

I'd seen enough of school from my doorstep to know I wouldn't like it, and I was sure those who were forced to go didn't like it either. Why else would they go in so quietly in the morning, then as soon as four o'clock came, erupt out of the gate laughing and shouting? I never heard anyone laughing and shouting when they were inside.

Terry jumped up. 'Right, I won, gimme your jink.'

I was horrified. 'What the 'ell are you talkin' about? You 'aven't won; I 'aven't had my go yet!' My diversionary tactics hadn't worked, but that was no reason for him to try cheating.

Taking careful aim, I spun my jink straight at Terry's. It landed on top, then rebounded and came to rest further away from the step than Terry's, a clear loser and the last of more than a dozen bottle-tops that Grandad had brought me from The Grosvenor pub, The Brick, at the top of Ritson Street, last Saturday. It had taken me hours to make them better to throw by folding over their crimped edges, and Terry had won the lot.

If my financial resources had run to a ha'penny, I would have put it inside the jink, on the cork seal, and folded the edges over it. That would have made it a deadly accurate 'six-hitter'. The chance of Terry winning, six times in a row, was so small you could forget about it, but I was broke, and a plea to my mother for a loan had fallen on deaf ears.

Terry however, had invested the remains of last week's pocket money in his six-hitter, and he'd cleaned me out. He picked up the jinks; then with a rare show of generosity, tossed one back to me. 'You can owe me that one till next week if you like, I've got plenty.' With that he thrust his hand in his trouser pocket and pulled out a fist-full of multi-coloured bottle-tops, most of them mine. He gloated over the mound before carefully counting them back into his pocket with tar-streaked fingers.

'Christ Almighty, your mam'll batter you when you gerrin; it's all over you, an' you'll 'ave to use butter to gerrit off.' Butter was the only known remover of tar, but butter was expensive. Not only that, it was rationed. He might have won all my jinks, but there would be a price to pay for gloating over my bad luck, when he got home. I cheered up a bit.

Just then the school bell rang. Suddenly the playground was full of the school's inmates, running about playing tick or climbing on the wall and thrusting their heads through the railings as though trying to savour freedom, some shouting minor obscenities at passers-by.

Others, more optimistic, begged the women heading to Lodgy for their shopping. 'Gerrus a penny barm cake from Williams's please, Missus; an' I'll give you the money for it later!'

Suddenly they fell silent. A second bell had sounded the end of their brief spell of freedom. I watched with a mixture of pity and derision as they lined up to be marched back into confinement. I reminded myself for the umpteenth time that school was definitely not for me.

It was a Thursday evening in September and we just had time for a go of 'Kick-the-Can' before I had to go in. We were playing opposite Ocklershaw's sweet shop, just in front of the school gates, when my mother appeared at our front door.

'Coo-ee Kenneth, I want you in, in five minutes!' For some reason or other she went on to threaten dire consequences if I tried to run away. Usually I could count on at least another ten minutes from the first summons, to the first threat of infanticide.

Tommy produced an empty tin and a jagged piece of plaster from the debbie. 'Right, keep still!' Billy, Georgie, their cousin Lily, Terry and me lined up in front of him. 'Dip-dip-dip, my blue ship, sailin' on the water, like-a cup an'-saucer, O, U, T spells OUT! You're 'It', Billy.'

Billy took the piece of plaster and chalked a large circle in the middle of the pavement, then carefully placed the tin, upright, in the centre of the circle. 'Ok Terry,' Billy instructed, 'you do it.'

Terry took a few steps back, then ran at the tin and kicked it as hard as he could. The tin flew for about ten yards, then rattled across the street, with Billy in hot pursuit, whilst the rest of us ran as fast as we could to get as far away from the circle as possible.

Billy caught up with the can, grabbed it, turned around without pausing and replaced it in the centre of the circle, then dashed off after Georgie who was lagging behind the rest of us. He caught him just before he disappeared into the jigger and punched him in the back. 'Tick! Gotcher, you bugger!'

Georgie pitched forward under the force of the blow, but managed to stay on his feet. Acknowledging his fate, he returned to stand inside the chalk circle.

Terry stood in the jigger alongside Ocklershaw's sweet shop, taunting Billy. 'Come on then, shi'y-arse! Worrare you waitin' for?' The taunt was too much for Billy. He made a dash for his tormentor, but failed to see Tommy crouching down behind the low wall at the end of the jigger. Billy shot past him in hot pursuit of Terry, leaving the circle unguarded. Tommy ran out, launched a kick at the can, missed, and dashed off with Georgie hot on his heels.

Billy spun round to see his captor running free and the can still upright in the circle. 'Ey, you, you bloody cheat, you 'aven't kicked the bloody can, so 'e's not allowed out of the den! Get back in you, Georgie, or I'll sodden-well marmalise you!' Billy was beetroot-red with rage.

Georgie stopped dead in his tracks. Being marmalised by Billy was a painful experience, not something you could ignore. He retraced his steps back to the circle. Before he was back in the den, I was summoned home by my mother. 'Yoo-hoo, Kenneth, I've told you, it's time to come in; an' I don't want you hiding, so come in now or I'll batter you!'

'Your Kenny's norr'ere, Mrs 'ayter.' Terry had re-appeared at the end of the jigger and instinctively assumed responsibility for providing an alibi. 'I 'aven't seen 'im for ages.' He shouted, ignoring the fact that I was standing alongside him. 'But I'll tell 'im when I see 'im.'

I thought hard for reasons why it would be impossible for me to obey for the next ten minutes or so, then I had second thoughts. It occurred to me that the street was becoming a dangerous place with all the threats of marmalising and battering, so I shouted a few insults at the others and ran home.

Friday morning dawned lovely and sunny. I couldn't wait to see who was playing out.

'I'm goin' out to play now, Mam!' I called down from the bedroom, where I was finishing getting dressed.

'Now don't be silly, Kenneth, you know you've got to go to school. I've told you dozens of times, so stop acting daft!' Mam shouted from the kitchen, her voice pitched high with exasperation.

The shock was traumatic. It must be true then! She'd been telling me for months that school started in September, but I never thought for a moment that it had anything to do with me. I knew Charlie was starting a new term that morning, because he was already half-dressed when I woke up. He was posing in front of the mirror admiring what he proudly advised was his special school outfit. A once white shirt with a separate fifteen-inch collar, donated by Uncle George, hung around Charlie's twelve-inch neck like a horse collar, exposing his Adam's Apple and half of his skinny chest. Grey long trousers with threadbare knees and a patch on the bottom completed his scholarly ensemble.

'Are you nearly dressed?' she shouted.

I just couldn't believe how persistent my mother was being. She knew very well I didn't want to go, I'd told her hundreds of times; so why on earth did she keep on insisting? I decided to remind her just one more time, before I went out to play.

'No, I don't wanner go today,' I replied, patiently. 'I'll see if I wanna go some other time, 'cause I'm goin' out to play with Terry now, Mam.'

'Terry won't be playing out either, he's going with you,' Mam replied, not so patiently. 'Now get ready or you'll be late!'

Christ, I'd forgotten that Terry said he was going. 'Well I'll play out with Tommy, then.' If she thought that Terry going might persuade me, she had another think coming.

'Tommy's going as well.' Her voice climbed higher up the scale. 'Now go and get ready, don't be silly. Wash your hands and face and put your clean shirt on. Christ Almighty, how many times do I have to tell you! Now get ready or I'll slaughter you.'

It seemed as though she needed a bit more time to get used to the idea that I wouldn't be going to school today, nor any other day for that matter, so I decided I would have to make a break for it. I'd come back at tea time and explain yet again that, whilst I had nothing against other people going, it would leave me with very little time to do what really mattered, like playing out.

I knew she would understand; she just needed a little more time. After all she was forever telling me that whatever she did, was best for me; even though she sometimes got a bit mixed up about exactly whose best interest she was serving. In fact, I should have told her last Friday that clouting me round the ears for breaking Mrs Callaghan's window was definitely not in my interest. Making a mental note to remind her about doing what was best for me as far as school was concerned, I hurriedly pulled on a pair of pumps and a jumper, then bolted down the stairs.

She was just coming out of the living room door when we met, side-on.

'Aarr! … You stupid little sod! … Frightened the sodden life out of me, you did! Warrare you doin'?' My mother grabbed me by the shoulder and shook me. Once again her reaction was not strictly in my best interest.

'I was only goin' out to find someone to play wiv, Mam. What I think is that, seein' as it's Friday, it's not worth goin' to school 'cause they're off on Sat'day, so I'll go out to play, then I can think about goin' to school on Monday.'

What I didn't know at the time was that Fridays were chosen for every-body's first day, so that the next day brought freedom again. Whether this was to break us in gently, or whether it was to drive home the message that, from hereon in, life was to be long runs of purgatory followed by a few hours of relief, I don't know.

She transferred her grip to my hand to prevent a last bid for freedom. 'It's five-t'nine, and you're not going to be sodden well late on your first day!' With that she dragged me through our front door and across the street.

The pavement outside the school was bustling with groups of Tiber Street School's mixed infants, all heading for the green gate. She brushed through them and hauled me through that dreaded gate, then on past rows of staring boys and girls, lined up on the playground, ready to be herded into the dark recesses of the school. Dazed and uncomprehending, I stumbled along until we reached a massive door, marked 'Infants'.

It was open.

By this time I was almost horizontal, with my heels cutting grooves in the concrete. But, with no thought for my wellbeing, she stepped inside, dragging me behind her.

'Name please!' I was dimly aware of a tall presence towering over me in the entrance hall. Still horizontal, I stared resolutely at the tiled floor.

'Come on young man, tell me your name.' The tall presence repeated the request.

I continued to stare at the floor. Why should I tell her my name? I didn't like her, whoever she was, and in any case there was no point because I wouldn't be staying.

'Tell the lady your name, Kenneth, like a good boy.' There was just a hint of menace in Mam's voice as she tried to cajole me. 'Come on now, stand up and be a good boy.' My mother smiled sweetly at the tall lady to indicate that there would be at least some measure of co-operation from the family, even if my sullen scowl suggested there would be none from me.

'Oh come on little man, it's really not too bad in here you know; you'll like it after a couple of days. Come on, tell me your name, I won't bite.' I was only half-aware of the kindly understanding smile on the tall lady's face.

Smiling or not, I was petrified of her. In any case I only had her word for it that she wouldn't bite, so I remained silent and sullen.

'His name's Kenneth, Miss, and he lives in Tagus Street.' My mother volunteered the information.

I was done for! My own mother, the same mother who said she did everything in my best interest, had sealed my fate. Escape was pointless, the tall lady now knew exactly where to find me. I was doomed.

Abject terror was replaced by a sense of overwhelming despair. After all those years living with someone who I thought, until this morning, was a loving mother, my fate was now in the hands of a complete stranger.

The tall lady took my hand and bent down to look me in the eyes. How strange, I thought. How strange that such an awful person should have such a lovely smile.

'Now then Kenneth, how would you like to meet the others in your class?' She studied a piece of paper in her hand, then made a tick on it. The tick, I realised, was me. I was recorded, registered; name and address: everything.

From now on, every move I made would be decided by some one other than me, recorded on a bit of paper and the paper sent to the next part of my life, with me following it.

My fate now rested with the tall lady with the lovely smile.

'Why don't you come back and take him home at lunchtime?' she turned to my mother. 'Don't worry, he'll be fine.' I was gently hauled to my feet. 'Now you come along with me Kenneth, I'll take you to meet your class-mates.' I found myself reluctantly studying my captor. She really did have such a lovely smile

That decided it: I would put my future in the tall lady's hands. After all, she wasn't the one who had dragged me from my home, from a life of freedom. In fact, she seemed to be trying to comfort me in the face of my mother's indifference. What was there to lose, now that my mother had deserted me?

She took me gently by the hand and led me along a broad corridor of high windows interspersed with forbidding heavy wooden doors, until we reached the end of the corridor and a door labelled 'Class 1'.

'Here we are, this is your classroom, now let's see if you already know anyone in your class.' She opened the door and gently propelled me into the room.

The classroom seemed enormous.

High windows formed a backdrop to parallel rows of wooden desks, set on a polished wood floor, sloping up and away from a wall festooned with scrawled crayoned pictures of matchstick mothers and dads outside houses half their size, with enormous orange splotches denoting sunny days. The rows of desks were all inhabited by silent, staring boys and girls. Mysterious charts with numbers and strange hieroglyphics all over them, hung from another wall. Standing in front of the pupils' desks and facing them, was a much bigger and higher desk and table.

'This is Kenneth, boys and girls, he lives in Tagus Street. Now say hello.' The tall lady cradled my chin in an attempt to divert my bright red embarrassment from the floor to the rows of desks.

The rows of faces remained silent, then, 'Hi-yer, Spud! Thought you said you wasn't comin'. Warrappened?' someone shouted from the back of the room.

It was Terry.

'Told you you'd 'ave to bloody-well come, didn' I?' he continued, a big grin on his face.

I began to survey the faces. They were all there, all my mates, every one of them. Terry, Tommy, Georgie, Billy: all of them. The sight of them cheered me up. At least I was locked up with friends.

'QUIET! Stand up whoever said that!' Another lady, dressed in a severe navy-blue suit, suddenly materialised from behind the big desk and surveyed the back row.

The class remained resolutely in their seats.

'I said stand up whoever said that. I know you are in the back row, so stand up. I will not have swearing in the classroom!'

Terry was about to stand up to see what all the fuss was about, but hesitated. The teacher had said something about swearing, and he had not sworn. However, he had shouted, and he was in the back row, so he decided he would stand up and advise her that she had misheard him.

'It was me as said 'ello to Spud, burr'I didn't swear. I was only tellin' Spud that I knew 'e'd 'ave to come to school, 'cause 'e reckoned 'e wouldn't bloody-well 'ave to, an' I said you sodden-well will, you know...'

'Sit down!' The lady holding my hand said something quietly to the teacher, before instructing Terry to resume his seat. Terry sat down, mystified. He only knew one swear word, as far as he was concerned, and he kept that for special occasions when there were no grown-ups about.

I was horrified. The teacher had got annoyed just because Terry had got up and said something politely, and was obviously going to do something to him if the lady with me had not stopped her. What would happen if you did something really wrong in school, like thumping someone? The consequences didn't bear thinking about.

I had been right all along, I knew I shouldn't have come.

Just wait till I told my mam what nearly happened to Terry. She'd have me out of here in no time.

Providing she got me out quickly, I was sure that, given enough time and maybe a bit of extra pocket money by way of a token of motherly love, I would forgive her temporary failure to look after my best interest.

'Right, now then, who wants Kenneth to sit by them?' The tall lady smiled at my classmates.

The silence was deafening.

'Oh, come on now, someone must want to sit by him?' she entreated the rows of staring faces. My lifelong friends stared silently at the teacher.

I couldn't believe it, all my best mates were sitting there and none of them wanted me near them. The horror of being in school began to be replaced by a sense of rejection. First my mother had abandoned me and now my friends. I wouldn't have minded so much, if I was going to have to sit by them for any length of time; but that was not the case, I would be going home for dinner soon, and I wasn't coming back.

'Well in that case I think he should sit...' The teacher looked around the desks for a vacant seat.

Before she selected one, Lily, Billy's cousin, put her hand up. 'Please Miss, he can sit next to me if nobody else will 'ave 'im,' Lily said without much enthusiasm. 'So long as 'e doesn't try to look up me skirt again like 'e did in our 'ouse, yesterday.'

The whole class giggled as I made my way up an aisle and along Lily's row, to sit down beside her. Lily shuffled along the seat to make room for me. The dark wooden desk had a hinged lid, stained with decades of dried ink, and carved with the initials of former inmates, some in crudely shaped hearts recording who loved whom, together with various messages relating their views on the teaching profession. A groove across the top contained a pen with its nib points bent in different directions, and an inkwell half full of black sludge.

'You can put your books in there.' Lily whispered, lifting the lid to reveal another ink stained message-laden surface.

'I 'aven't got no bloody books to purrin', so it's no bloody good to me, is it.' I said, not realising just how much the voice would carry in such a large room.

'Kenneth, if you swear again, I'll send you to the Headmistress!' The teacher strode up the aisle towards me.

I was as baffled as Terry. What was she on about, swearing? Like Terry, I only knew one swear word, it was the same one as he knew and began with an 'f'; in fact it was me that taught him it. Again, like Terry, I only used it on special occasions, and, whilst this was such an occasion, I didn't have the courage to use it with adults present, even though I'd never see them again.

The teacher returned to the front of the class, perhaps accepting that she had to give some leeway to the new starters, or maybe realising it was a hopeless situation.

'Right! Pay attention everybody! I'm going to call the register. When you hear your name, you must stand up and say, "Present, Miss!"'

She took a large ledger out of her desk and began to intone our names. 'George Applet…, Mary Cunning…,' The names were called in alphabetical order, each name accompanied by the required response, 'Present, Miss!' until she got to me.

'Kenneth …'

'Present, Miss,' I responded, before she finished, 'but I'm goin' 'ome in a minute.' She ignored me and continued through the register.

Just as she finished, a bell rang.

Bang! … bang! … bang! Three dozen desk tops slammed down and Class 1 threw themselves down the aisles, along the window-lined corridor and out to the playground. Within seconds, all the other classes erupted through the Infants door. Then there was a frenzied rush to start and finish all kinds of games before a second bell announced the end of freedom.

One group of girls produced a pair of long skipping ropes. A girl at either end, with a rope in each hand, twirled them in high circles in opposite directions, chanting in strict time with the circling ropes. 'Tinker, Tailor, Soldier, Sailor. Rich Man, Poor Man, Beggar Man, Thief! as another two leapt into the twirling ropes.

Suddenly, and magically, each rope reversed direction.

The two girls skipping inside the circling ropes tripped as they failed to keep up with the changing rhythm, and fell on top of each other in a tangle of rope and legs; their knickers on display to the whole of Tiber Street Mixed Infants.

Terry and I were leaning morosely against the drinking fountain in the playground shelter. Georgie dashed over, brandishing a rubber ball. 'I bags we play "Re-Ally-Oh", an' I'll dip to see who's "it".'

'Who says you can dip?' Terry demanded.

'I says,' Georgie retorted. 'It's my bloody ball!' There was no arguing

82

with that, so we lined up in front of him. 'Eany, Meany, Miney, Mo. Sat the baby on the po. When he hollers, let 'im go. Eany, Meany, Miney, Mo. I'm "It"!' With that, Georgie hurled the ball against the wall under the shelter, yelled 'Spud!', then with the rest of the gang, ran like hell towards the far side of the playground.

It wasn't fair, I was still traumatised by the treachery of my mother, and missed catching the ball before it hit the ground, after rebounding from the wall. I was furious: now I wasn't allowed to hurl it back at the wall and call someone else's name.

'That wasn't bloody fair, that wasn't!' Further words failed me, there was simply no justice in this awful place. I ran after the ball, grabbed it, and yelled 'STOP!' The others stopped running and turned to face me. The rotten sods were right over the other side of the playground. There was no way the prescribed hop, skip and a jump, would take me within accurate throwing distance; but I had no choice. I took a short illegal run and bounded towards Billy, the nearest; and threw the ball.

Billy stepped sideways, and the ball just missed him.

'You bloody cheated, you did! You moved your feet, you cheatin' sod! That's not fair, I'm gunner have another throw.'

Fortunately the others agreed, so I collected the ball and retraced my steps to where I'd been, more or less.

'You wasn't there!' Billy was furious. 'You're tryin' to cheat, you were miles further away!'

I compromised by taking a few steps back, then hurled the ball while Billy was still counting my steps. It hit him right in the middle of his chest.

'Oww! That 'urt, that did!' Billy yelled, but I never heard him. I was off at a fast run to hide around the corner by the Seniors' entrance. Billy grabbed the ball and ran over to the shelter to hurl it against the wall.

'Terry!' he yelled.

Terry dashed over to try and catch the ball. He almost made it, when the bell went. The frenetic playing of the Mixed Infants stopped immediately. Then, like automatons, they lined up and trooped through the Infants door and back to their classes.

This was my chance to escape. There was not a teacher in sight. The railings were no problem, I had scaled them many a time, to get into the playground at weekends. This time I would be going the other way.

I was half way up the railings, when the tall lady with the lovely smile appeared at the doorway.

'I see you have forgotten your way to your classroom, Kenneth. Well never mind, come on, I'll take you again.' I was lost to her smile and meekly returned to the door. She took my hand and delivered me back to Class 1.

'Here's your friend back, Lily.' She gently propelled me up the aisle to my desk.

"E's not my friend, Miss. I don't like 'im and me mam told me not to play wiv 'im 'cause she doesn't like 'im either. I only said 'e could sit by me 'cause Mary dared me to. An' 'e sat wiv me before, so I won the dare; but I don't want 'im sitting by me again.'

Lily moved to my side of the desk to stop me sitting down. I stood forlornly by the desk. Nobody wanted me, not my friends, not even own mother. Now even Lily didn't want me and she was notorious for liking boys.

The lady looked around the class and spotted an empty desk. 'There we are, Kenneth. Sit there for now and we'll find somebody later to sit with.'

Alone and lonely, I sat down and stared down at the desk-top. After a couple of minutes the teacher with the severe suit came into the room, her arms festooned with different coloured bands of narrow ribbons.

'Right, pay attention, class! I'm going to put you into different teams: Red Team, Green Team, Yellow Team and Blue Team.'

She consulted the register and began calling out names, telling them to come down to her and collect their ribbon and put it over their left shoulder and across the body to loop around the opposite hip.

One by one we trooped down the aisle. Red, Green, Yellow, Blue, Red, Green. Then it was my turn: I was Yellow. Sullen despair at being rejected by all those dearest to me, was replaced by a feeling of deep humiliation. Yellow! I couldn't believe it. Red should have been my colour, blood-red, the colour of a real team. I had been put in the Yellow Team! Yellow, the colour of cowardice. A yellow ribbon around my waist: Yellow-belly, I would be branded yellow-belly for the rest of my life! My career as a gang leader was over, though I suppose it didn't really matter, seeing that my followers had cast me out anyway.

Returning to my lonely desk I folded my arms on the lid, to rest my weary head. Life had dealt a series of terrible blows.

Yesterday I was free; in fact, carefree: the leader of a gang with the whole of Liverpool 8 as our territory. Now I was locked up behind the green gate, alone and unloved, a prisoner in solitary confinement for the rest of my life, with a yellow ribbon round me. I began to sob. I wanted my mam. The trouble was, she didn't want me.

Suddenly, a bell sounded. The three dozen desk lids bang! bang! banged down again, and the whole class headed for the door, fighting and scrambling to get out first, leaving me alone in the classroom.

The teacher was on her way out carrying the register, when she noticed me. 'It's time to go for lunch, Kenneth, your mother will be waiting for you.' I peered at her through the tears, my chin still resting on the desk.

'Lunchtime Kenneth, off you go, your mother will be expecting you,' she repeated.

Then she realised I was crying and walked up the aisle to me, to kneel down alongside my desk. 'It really isn't such a bad place, you know. All the children like it after a few days, and you have to learn to read and write, so you can get a good job when you grow up, won't you? So don't cry, you'll soon get to like it and your mother wouldn't like to see you upset now, would she?'

Someone had told me that teachers knew everything. Well this one didn't. For a start there was simply no way I'd ever get to like it, in any case I wasn't going to try because I wasn't going back after lunch, whatever lunch was. Secondly, you didn't need to be any good at reading or writing to get a good job. Charlie, my elder brother wasn't much good and he was going to be a famous Ballet Dancer, I'd seen him practicing; and he reckoned Ballet Dancers got loads of money, and drove big cars. If that wasn't enough, she seemed to think my mother wouldn't want to see me upset. Well that was a laugh, it was all my mother's doing: she was the one who had wrecked my life by dragging me in here in the first place.

A fat lot this teacher knew.

I glanced at the teacher, thinking perhaps that I should enlighten her on the subject of school, Charlie's career plans and my mother's complete disregard for my happiness. Her face was level with mine, and when I glanced at her I looked straight into her eyes: kindly smiling, understanding eyes.

'Come on now, Kenneth, I'll take you to the gate, your mother will be waiting there for you.'

Wrong again, I thought, my mam will be in the pub by now. But I said nothing; her eyes were just too nice and I felt I couldn't burden her with all my problems. It was obvious that she liked me and I just did not want to upset her.

She put her arm round my shoulder, then gently but firmly pulled me to my feet, leading me through the door, across the playground, to the open green gate.

I could hardly believe my eyes! There was my mam, standing just outside the gate. The teacher and my mother, unnoticed by me, exchanged knowing smiles as my mother took my hand. We walked in silence to our front door, where she let go of my hand.

I stumbled through the door and into the cosy familiarity of the house. I was back where I belonged.

The trauma of the day's events hit me the moment I opened our living room door. I burst out crying and flung myself face down on the sofa.

'I don't like it in school, Mam!' I bawled. 'I don't wanner go back, I wanner go out to play!' The words fought for a place between deep body-wrenching sobs. 'I don't 'ave to go back, do I Mam? I don't wanner learn to read an' write, I don't wanna good job, I'll 'ave one like me dad.' I buried my head in the cushion, trying to hide from the awful prospect of my mam again abrogating her responsibility for my happiness, by taking me back to that terrible place.

'Here we are, Kenneth, have one of these to eat, you like these.' She offered a big square tin of broken biscuits for me to take my pick.

So that was her game; she was trying to bribe me. Well she wouldn't succeed, but I saw no reason to refuse the offer and see just how far she would go with her underhand tactics. I took three, carefully choosing ones that were nearly whole. She didn't say a word, so I took another one. Even then she said nothing, but simply smiled and said. 'You must be hungry dear, it must be all the things you've learned in school. I knew you were a clever little man.'

It was unbelievable, the length she was prepared to go to, to get me back to school. But she had no chance. Bribery and flattery would get her nowhere.

She kept looking at the clock, deducting twenty minutes off the time shown to allow for the loose minute finger. One o'clock came and I was still munching my way through her bribes. Our front door was still open, so we could hear the school bell and the chattering inmates making their way back to confinement.

My mother began to look a little uncomfortable. 'Time to go back, Kenneth, don't forget all your friends will have gone back, so you don't want to be the odd one out, do you?'

Friends, what friends? She had got this ploy wrong: I was already the odd one out. Everyone else had someone sitting by them. Nobody wanted me. Not only that, but I was in the yellow-belly team.

Grabbing one last biscuit, I buried my head back in the cushion, and started to sob my heart out. My mother sat on the edge of the sofa, completely at a loss for what to do for the best.

'Are you in there, Spud?' The living room door burst open and there stood Lily. 'Miss says I 'ave to come and get you 'cause you're the only one who 'asn't come back after dinner. An' she says you 'ave to sit by me.'

'Well isn't that nice, Kenneth? Lily wants to sit next to you. Come on then, or Lily will be upset.' My mother seized the chance.

'No, Missus 'ayter, I don't wanner sit by 'im, nobody does. Teacher says I 'ave to, even though I don't like 'im, and nobody else likes 'im either 'cause...'

My mother hurriedly interrupted any further discussion of my unpopularity. 'Well it's very nice of you anyway, Lily, isn't it Kenneth? Now be a good boy and go with Lily!' There was a definite hint of menace in her tone. I seemed to be getting a bit unpopular with her as well.

I thought quickly. Then I had an idea. I'd go back to school, which I knew would only be for a few hours, spend the weekend playing out, then run away from home first thing Monday morning. Woolton seemed the best bet. I would go and live off the land in Woolton. Charlie, my older brother, had been there lots of times, stealing apples from the gardens of big houses. He had made no mention of any schools in the area, so it sounded a perfect place to live a life of solitary freedom: plenty of food and no school to get locked up in.

Still sobbing, I reluctantly rolled off the sofa and stood up.

Lily took me firmly by the hand and led me out of the house, through the green gate and back to Class 1, letting go of my hand when we drew alongside my lonely desk. I took the hint and sat down, all alone and very lonely.

'Oh good, now Kenneth's here, we are all present.' The teacher made no comment on my late arrival. 'Right children, I want to tell you a little about what we will be learning over the next few weeks.'

She began a long monologue about the wonders of Times Tables, pointing at the mysterious charts hanging on the walls, and telling us we would have to memorise the meaningless numbers on them.

But it wasn't all numbers, she assured us, because we would also read about the antics of Janet and John.

A few examples of how to spell common words were thrown in to excite us, but where she got her ideas from I just don't know. If you used her spelling you would end up with a pronunciation bearing no resemblance at all to the way we spoke.

Then she explained about morning assembly, and registers, and how important it was to be punctual.

At last, she concluded her description of our torture for the coming weeks by advising us that, because it was our first day, we could go home early.

I just couldn't see the point of anything she said. I didn't know a Janet or a John; they certainly didn't live in our street, so they were of no interest to me whatsoever. As far as the Times Tables were concerned, they weren't much use to me either. I only got a tanner a week pocket money, so there was no need to count beyond six.

But the going home early idea, that was different! My spirits lifted even higher; I would have more time to prepare for Monday's departure to a life in Woolton Woods.

The teacher sat down at her desk and began studying the register. 'Right, pay attention children, just before you go. We seem to have more in the yellow team than we do in the red, so I'll have to make a change to even up the numbers. Is there anyone in the yellow team who would like to move to the red team?'

My hand was aloft before she finished her sentence.

'Good boy, Kenneth, it's nice to see someone has volunteered. Bring me your yellow ribbon and take this red one.'

At last there was a slight change to my fortunes.

I was on my way back to my desk, proudly bearing a bright red sash, when Lily put her hand up. 'Please Miss, you said Kenny was supposed to sit wiv me, an' 'e's sat by 'imself again. You can sit wiv me if you like, Spud.' She waved to me to join her. The change from a yellow-belly to blood-red team member was already paying dividends.

Before I could respond, there was a scuffle on the back row. Terry elbowed his neighbour out of his seat.

'Eh Spud, there's room 'ere next to me!'

I scrambled over the row of seats and sat down beside him; ignoring Lily's invitation. She had her chance before playtime and she had blown it.

Billy got up from his seat in the third row back and ran to the desk next to Terry. 'Bugger off you.' Its occupant buggered off and Billy sat down across the aisle alongside me, a big grin on his face. The teacher watched the toing and froing out of the corner of her eye, pretending not to notice.

My rehabilitation was now complete: I was a member of the Red Team, and back at the centre of our gang.

The bell rang at half past three. Hundreds of desk tops crashed down throughout the school as hundreds of Infants and Junior Mixed made a frenzied dash for a weekend of freedom.

Come Monday, I had decided against a hunter-gatherer's life in the wilderness around Woolton Woods. All through the weekend I kept thinking of the tall lady's lovely smile, and my bright red sash.

Having told my mam about the mysterious numbers on the charts, she explained that they were the same as the sums that she had taught me, and that Janet and John were only fictional characters in books; a bit like in Enid Blyton's, but more grown up.

Well I could already count up to a hundred with a bit of prompting and I'd been getting fed up with Noddy, who was just too good to be true, never chasing girls or throwing bricks. I quite looked forward to a good book with a bit of action, so reading might not be so bad after all. As for the Times Tables, they were going to be a doddle.

Apart from resolving the problems with school lessons, it looked as though I'd taught Mam a lesson. She went back to being the loving mother I was entitled to, even producing the biscuit box again, and saying nothing when I chanced a whole handful. Maybe I'll give it one more go on Monday, I advised her, reaching in the tin for another handful.

Monday came and I went to school, and I continued to go for another six, mostly happy, years. Memories of those years in school are a little hazy, but some have lasted a lifetime. For example, the occasional visit to solitary confinement, for ten awful minutes: sitting on the bench in the short corridor outside the Head's office, waiting to be summoned in. On one such occasion I was advised that playing in the gym, down the steps of the airy in the yard, was not allowed, especially when the school was closed for the weekend and the gymnasium door was locked. Two strokes of the cane emphasised the 'not allowed' bit of the advice.

Or the celebration of Empire Day, when we all paraded on the playground in straight lines to be presented with an orange and a small paper bag full of cocoa, which came from 'the far flung reaches of His Majesty King George VI's Empire.' Just before the presentation, I had to put up my hand in order to satisfy a particularly desperate call of nature. The Head must have decided His Majesty's Empire was more important than my problem, and ignored me. A little yellow stream wended its way from between my feet, down through the pupil's rows, to form a small pool in front of the bearer of the fruits of His Majesty's Empire.

I was in solitary confinement again next day.

The journey that started from that first day at school took me from the Infants to the Seniors and eventually to the dreaded '11+' Examination. It says much for the expertise and dedication of the teachers of Tiber Street School, that I managed to pass; certainly I cannot claim any credit.

The teachers overcame complete apathy on my part, with a mixture of extraordinary teaching skills and threats to my person. They managed to ensure I had some idea of what numbers were and could read and write, at least insofar as I found the right room number for the examination, and spelt my name properly on top of the test paper.

The examination itself is a vague half-memory, but the result of my effort is vivid in the memory: I managed a 'recall'. In other words, I was a borderline case, neither a 'pass' nor a 'fail', or maybe I just failed and the examiner felt sorry for me. A 'recall' meant you had to go for an interview at the Education Offices in Sir Thomas Street.

I had not the faintest idea as to why I was dressed up in my Sunday best when it was a Tuesday, nor did I have a clue why I was up waiting outside an enormous wooden door in the Education Offices in the July of 1950.

'Come in!' A man's sombre, mechanical sounding voice summoned me into the room beyond the forbidding door. Petrified, I stood up and pushed the door. Nothing happened.

'Come in!' It was the same mechanical voice, only louder. I pushed the door as hard as I could, this time turning its large polished brass knob.

The heavy door swung open, with me clutching the knob. I ended up on my knees inside the room with my back to the mechanical voice, still clinging to the doorknob.

'Stand up boy!' The voice now seemed more frustrated than sombre or mechanical.

I almost passed out with fright, but then a more gentle, lady's voice asked. 'Are you alright Kenneth? It is Kenneth, isn't it?' I regained a little of my composure at the sound of a human being, and stood up.

Plucking up a bit more courage, I turned round.

The room was enormous. Oak panels lined the walls right up to the ornate moulded ceiling, with great oil paintings of be-wigged dignitaries and, for some reason or other, horses. Right in the middle of the room, looming over me, was a splendid table with two men and a woman sitting behind it. The woman indicated a tiny chair in front of the desk for me to sit on.

I sat down, bolt upright in the chair, and looked up at the table. The table was almost all I could see; it was so high and my chair so low. I could only just make out the balding tops of the two men's heads.

'Why don't you move your chair back a little, so that we can see you?' The tone in the sombre voice suggested the speaker thought he was talking to an idiot. Still in a daze, I half stood up, pulled the chair up underneath me, and shuffled backwards, catching my heel on the edge of the carpet.

'Aaarr … sodden 'ell!' I dropped the chair, tripped over it and performed a backward somersault, landing in a heap on the floor. A voice from somewhere over the table suggested I get up again, sit down, and stay sitting down.

The panel of three then launched a series of questions at me: something like what nine eights might be, and how to spell a few words of one or two syllables. They then got onto the subject of my interests, that is interests within school rules and the law of the land. As such, the scope of the questions was pretty limited, but, some how or other, they knew I was interested in animals. It was my last hope, having advised them that nine eights were a hundred and forty seven, and that 'colour' was spelt with a 'k' and ended in 'er'.

They only asked two questions:

'What,' the man with sombre voice asked, 'is a thrush's anvil?'

'What,' the lady wanted to know, 'is special about tadpoles?'

Suddenly I felt at ease. The memory of a friend I once knew came flooding back to mind. He was a park keeper in Sefton Park who walked with a limp. Small in stature, he wore an enormous uniform that made him look as though he had no hands or feet, and a peaked cap many sizes too big for him.

Limping Johnny had told me all about birds and their habits; and I had seen for myself what was special about frogs and taddies, in a secret little pond in the Fairy Glen, shown to me and my mate Terry by Limping Johnny.

So I was able to answer their questions in considerable detail, more than they wanted to hear, I suppose. I told them that a thrush's anvil was any stone he could find to batter snail shells to pieces, so he could eat their guts. And I told them that men frogs climbed on the back of lady frogs and did something which had the same name as a swear word I knew. But I advised them that I wasn't allowed to tell them what the word was because my mam said she would batter me to pieces if I ever used it again.

I went on to explain how all this action resulted in great dollops of frog-spawn, which turned into little tadpoles; except that some of it was eaten by birds if they couldn't find a stone to bash up the snails.

I finished up by telling them that the taddies eventually grew legs and became big frogs, and they immediately started to climb on each other's backs and set about doing the thing that my mam said she would marmalise me for saying.

Some weeks later, all the children leaving school that year were assembled in one of the classrooms. The awesome Mrs Bell, the Headmistress, presided over the occasion.

We were there to learn who had been successful in the '11+' examination.

One by one, those who had passed were given a note and told to run home and give it to their parents. They were called in alphabetical order and I wasn't even listening when she got to the 'H's'.

Having discovered that eight nines were less than a hundred and 'colour' had couple of 'o's in it, I reckoned my chances of enjoying a higher education were close to zero and would be wasted anyway.

But I was wrong, I passed.

A week or two later we had a presentation day. Prizes were given to those who were leaving the school just opposite my house, to go on to higher education and achieve great things. They gave me a prize as well, a book: *The Mystery of the Island* by Isobel Knight.

This was my last day at Tiber Street County School.

Postscript

My story was to have ended here, but then I learned that Tiber Street School was to close its doors to schoolchildren in the summer of 1999, though the splendid red brick and yellow stone building, the shell of our school, will survive.

Within the fabric of the building there must remain the echoes of its past: the chanting of a thousand times tables, the laughter of children at play in the schoolyard, and perhaps some tears. These echoes are part of the history of an institution that served the communities around Lodge Lane for the best part of a century, echoes that would have been lost but for the efforts of a dedicated group of people closely associated with the school.

The Tiber Parents Editorial group has immortalised our school in their book, *The History Of A Liverpool Community School, 1904–1999* by Iria Dyson, Linda Harwood, Antonia Mercer and Lesley Topping, Editor: Ray Costello, of Liverpool Parent School Partnership published in conjunction with Countyvise Limited, Birkenhead.

The historians were kind enough to include a story or two of mine, and for that I feel very proud. In an attempt to thank them for their work, I have added this postscript and would like to dedicate the story of a Tiber Street Mixed Infant to them. I just hope they don't mind!

Tomorrow

'I'm getting inoculated against dip ... dip something or other,
dip ... dip ... diphtheria, that's it, diphtheria.'

Gentle Jesus, meek and mild,
Look upon a little child,
Pity my simplicity,
Suffer me to come to thee.

CHARLES WESLEY

Diphtheria Clinic

THE STREET WAS ALIVE WITH GOSSIP.

It was a dusty sunny day and small knots of women were gathered outside a number of houses on either side of the street. All were chattering and none listening. The words of the more strident seemed to hang in the warm air.

I could not find anyone to play out with, so I had carried Tibby, our cat, to the front doorstep. Tibby nurtured a busy horde of fleas which, when they ran out of room on Tibby, dined on Charlie and me. It was my job to cull their numbers to the point where they could all enjoy full stomachs without having to seek new pastures.

A pan of water was already on the doorstep for making sure the captured insects stayed captured and eventually met their maker.

'Wouldn't you think she'd have done it? I don't know how she lives with herself.' It was my mam's turn to get a few words in. 'She just doesn't care that one, never has. 'Ave you seen 'er kitchen ... never ever gets a lick of paint near it ... and 'er curtains! ... well ...' Words failed her for a brief moment. 'All she can think about is her hairdo.'

'Too busy gallivanting about, if you ask me,' agreed Mrs Murphy.

'Maybe it's a blessing in disguise,' Mrs Jones added wisely. 'She never fed him prop'ly anyway, from what I could see. Just filled 'im up with rubbishy cakes and things to shut 'im up ... never cooked anything proper for 'im.'

They all nodded in agreement, whilst my mother poked the step with her yard-brush to emphasise the point.

Their conversation floated over my head as I turned Tibby onto her back and tickled her tummy to fool her into thinking the cull was a game. The fleas dodged sideways out of the furrows I made in Tibby's fur. Some were a bit slow off the mark or got road-blocked by others in the queue.

'Gotcha, you little bugger!' I caught one between pinched finger and thumb and dropped it in the pan to join a dozen or so others revolving round and round in their first and last swim.

My mother broke off the conversation. 'You mind your language you, you little sod.' She jabbed me with the brush. 'And mind what you're doing with that pan. If you dint it, I'll marmalise you. Anyway, what are you using that one for? I'll need it for the chips in a minute; now hurry up and finish what you're doing.' She returned to the discussion.

After about twenty fleas had joined in the circular formation swimming, the task began to get boring, so I let Tibby go. She shot straight back down the lobby, through the house and leapt onto the backyard wall to join her friends and replenish the stocks.

I followed her down the yard and carefully flushed the contents of the pan down the toilet. Tibby had jumped across to the backyard wall on the other side of the jigger to register her interest with a scruffy battle-scarred tom. They sat on the backyard wall where Little Arthur used to live.

There was not much else to do so I used the bin in the wall for a toe-hold and climbed up onto the lavatory roof. Sitting there, I had a good view into Arthur's yard, but of course there was no sign of Arthur.

The familiar things in his yard and the glimpse into his living room through partly drawn curtains reminded me of when we used to have a competition to see who was growing up the fastest. Tears welled in my eyes as I wondered where Little Arthur was now.

Arthur was in fact about the same height as me, even though he was a bit younger, but my mother called him Little Arthur because she felt sorry for him. He was an only child and from what I could gather, he was a nuisance to his mother because he had to be fed and clothed.

Nobody seemed sure about what had happened to his dad, but rumour had it that he had insisted on being fed as well, and that was his downfall.

Arthur's mother evicted him from the household just after Arthur was born. But it wasn't so easy to evict Arthur. As often as not his mother would be out when Arthur came home from school, so he would sit on the back doorstep waiting for her, in all weathers.

'Go and see if Little Arthur's on the step,' my mother would say to me. 'Tell him to come in and wait.'

Arthur and I would then sit in front of the fire with a cup of water and a sugar butty. He loved my mam's sugar butties: they were the nearest thing he got to something homemade.

Occasionally mother and I would be invited to Arthur's for tea, something I looked forward to with excitement. He had dozens of toys, bought to keep him quiet, according to Mam. Most of them were clockwork and some still worked. Not only that, but real cakes, from Williams' Bakery, came with the tea.

There was a bang on the backyard door.

'You there Spud?' A small voice shouted from the jigger, ''s that you?'

It was a few months before the war against Tibby's fleas and I was in our backyard watering the marigolds that Mam had planted in a window box. I was no horticultural expert, but they all looked beyond help to me. However, my mother had delegated the job of looking after them to me, so I was hoping against hope that a milk bottle full of life-giving water would save the flowers and with them my bacon.

'I've come to 'ave a go at the bolt, Spud,' Arthur shouted over the wall.

Arthur had got it into his head that he was growing up faster than me and was determined to prove it by being the first to reach the top bolt on our kitchen door. At least once a week he would ask if he could have a try.

I left the marigolds in the hands of God and unlatched the back door. He dashed through the door, up the yard and into the kitchen.

I was horrified. 'I do it first, it's my bloody bolt!' I shouted after him. Arthur waited obediently as I took up position behind the door and stretched up on tiptoe. 'Done it!' I gasped triumphantly, and collapsed back down. I had just managed to touch the handle on the bolt.

Arthur looked crestfallen but duly took his place, flat against the door. His face turned beetroot-red as he clawed his fingers up the door to the bolt. Then with a final upward lunge, he reached the bolt and thrust it home. 'So 'ave I, so 'ave I!' He shrank back to his normal length.

I was mortified. I was convinced I would win.

'What you do that for?' I demanded. 'What did you push the bloody bolt for; now we can't gerrout!'

Just as I was about to declare his bolt touching as not counting because he'd locked us in, my mother appeared from the living room.

'Hello little Arthur,' she smiled fondly at him. 'Is our Kenny cheating again?'

She must have been referring to the time I had won with the help of a flat iron brought into position under foot whilst Arthur was intent on watching my fingers.

'No 'e wasn't this time Aunty May, 'cause we've drawn. We've both reached it together.'

'No we didn't,' I countered, 'I did it first, you were last, so I won fair an' square.'

Arthur's mouth dropped open at this undeniable fact. He turned to Mam for support. ''E only touched it Aunty May; I shoved it locked.' His big blue eyes glistened with tears.

'Yes, an' you locked us in didn't you? I didn't shove it 'cause I didn' wanna lock us in did I?' Satisfied that I had destroyed his claim to a draw, I turned to Mam for adjudication.

'Alright smart-arse, Arthur reached it and locked it, so you reach it and unlock it!' She glared at me.

I generously conceded a draw.

'Well done Arthur,' she patted him on the head. ''Ere you are, have a piece of this.' She produced a piece of cinder toffee. Arthur gratefully popped it into his mouth.

'You've had enough!' she ignored my outstretched palm. 'I'm going shopping now,' she announced, 'so you two behave yourselves like good boys.'

'Me mam says would you like to come for tea tonight?' said Arthur, suddenly remembering the real reason for his visit.

There was a pause. 'That would be nice, Arthur,' she lied. 'What time did she say?'

Arthur was not sure about that, but in a flash of inspiration replied, 'Tea-time Aunty May, please.'

'Right, oh!' my mother smiled. 'If I'm not too busy, we'll be over about four o'clock.' My mother's social diary was usually not too full, so I looked forward to cakes and clockwork trains.

Arthur and I whiled away the rest of the afternoon in a variety of pursuits. He was not allowed to keep pets of any kind. 'Messy, 'orrible smelly things,' was his mother's view of all God's creatures; a view that embraced children, according to my mother, particularly Arthur. You felt that Arthur knew he was something of a nuisance to his mother and that was why he was always quiet and placid at home, trying never to get noticed.

'Can we play with Tibby?' Arthur loved our cat.

As soon as Tibby saw us approaching she slunk off towards the kitchen door, but the door was shut. There was no escape and I grabbed her. Tibby hissed and growled, struggling furiously until she broke free and bolted under the settee in the living room, pausing only to scratch Arthur's face as she leapt from my arms.

'Ow! That didn' 'alf 'urt, that did,' he rubbed the angry-red claw mark.

I examined the wound, explaining to Arthur that cat scratches always turned poisonous, with the victim invariably dropping dead in a few minutes.

A few minutes later Arthur was still alive, though rather pale. I waiting a while longer just to make sure there was no delayed reaction, but no, Arthur's face was recovering some of its colour.

Somewhat disappointed, I suggested we go into the backyard and have a look at the rest of my pets. Usually I had a collection of tadpoles or even a frog, but today all I could offer was a jar with some captive caterpillars and a dead spider, and a matchbox with a resident cockroach.

We examined the jar. 'Caterpillars must 'ave killed it,' I decided, gently prodding the spread-eagled spider, hoping for signs of life. 'They'll prob'ly eat it in a minute.'

Arthur, whose knowledge of a caterpillar's diet was about as good as mine, stared expectantly at the writhing grubs. 'Well, gerronwivit,' he instructed, 'if you're gunner eat the sodden thing, eat it ... gerronwivit!'

The caterpillars were obviously not hungry and ignored him. We lost interest.

There was nothing else for it. 'We'll 'ave a game of Gerries,' I announced. 'An' I bags goin' first.'

Unlike Arthur, my collection of toys was somewhat limited: two racing cars made out of lead with several wheels missing, a chess set bought for me by Charlie, for Christmas, but which I couldn't play, and assorted pieces of Meccano. But best of all was a toy cannon gun that fired special missiles. And it actually worked, often to devastating effect.

'Gerries' was based on Grandad's vivid accounts of the Luftwaffe's attempts to bomb the Liverpool Docks and the Dockers who worked there. Grandad worked on the docks, on the odd occasion when he was picked from the daily queue of hopefuls standing outside the Dock Gates, and he enthralled us with his stories of danger and devotion to duty as a professional Docker.

Grandad assured us that he wasn't bothered about the constant dangers he faced. Even the threat of incineration by German incendiary bombs didn't worry him, because he saw it as his duty to save thousands of tons of shipping whilst rescuing hundreds of dockers from the infernos that raged along the Dock Road.

We hung on his every word; so much so that, when I first heard the Liverpool folk song about those times, which goes something like '...thank God said me old man, the Pier Head's still there', I thought it was all about Grandad.

The game of Gerries needed bits of Meccano to make up dockyard buildings, whilst the gun was the Luftwaffe. The red and green pieces were stacked precariously against one another and subjected to a bombardment from a range of about six inches by the cannon. The winner was the one who flattened the pile in the least number of shots.

We charged into the living room. I extricated my box of toys from the big brass box at one end of the fire tender, then dumped the contents of the box on the table and stacked up a range of dock buildings.

If you counted the total number of shots fired, Arthur won; but if you only counted the ones that hit the target, then I won. It was my gun and my Meccano, so I won.

We were still debating the rules when my mother arrived back. 'You two wash your hands and face and we'll go round to Arthur's for tea,' she announced. Arthur obeyed at once, and disappeared into the kitchen. I followed reluctantly, having failed to convince Mam that you didn't have to wash faces, because you didn't use them for anything.

Mother put on some lipstick and freshened up the rouge on her cheeks, then we followed her down the yard and across the jigger to Arthur's back door.

'We're 'ere, we're 'ere Mam!' Arthur pressed his face to the locked door. After a few moments, high heels clacked down the tiled yard and the door bolts slid open.

Mrs Hughes stood there in a short flowered dress, silk stockings and hair piled up in hundreds of carefully placed curls, all exactly the same size like tight coils of fine wire, tinged a slight orange colour. She surveyed Arthur as you would a lower life form. 'I do wish you wouldn't shout, luv. An' 'ow many times 'ave I told you it's Mam-a, not Mam.' She pronounced the 'a' as an emphasised 'ar'. 'Aren't they terrible, May?' she turned to my mother. 'You try terribly 'ard to get them to speak proper, don't you, and worrappens?' She smiled sweetly at me. 'And how's our Arthur's best friend?' she asked.

Well I thought Arthur's best friend was Henry Cartwright who lived next door to him. ''E's alright I think, Mrs Hughes, 'cept 'e's got a bloody big boil on 'is arse,' I replied.

My mother didn't hear me; she couldn't take her eyes off the permanent waves that sat immovably on Mrs Hughes' head as she clacked back up the yard.

Tea went very well as far as I was concerned, but my mother ate nothing, later advising me that mice and cockroaches got first bite of anything in Mrs Hughes' kitchen. Try as I might, I could see no connection between the state of a kitchen and the taste of cakes that came from the bakery on Lodge Lane. Anyway, so what? You couldn't blame the mice; the cakes were delicious.

Arthur got his toys out: a genuine Hornby train set, an assortment of racing cars and a monkey with a side drum that went berserk when you wound it up. We joined up the railway track on the mat in front of the sooty fire range with its few pieces of coal struggling to stay alight.

The light from the single small window began to fade.

My mother quickly forgot her dislike and perhaps envy of Arthur's mother. Their low-pitched conversation soon began to systematically destroy the reputation of our neighbours. Their gossip formed the background to my cries of triumph as I dislodged the engine from its track with carefully timed aims of the fully wound up racing cars, in a new version of Gerries.

The light continued to fade until it was time to ignite the gas lamp hanging from a plaster rose in the centre of the ceiling.

Mrs Hughes hated lighting the gas because once, a long time ago, she lit the oven some minutes after turning it on. The event had forced her confinement indoors until the Henna had re-established its influence over her singed hair, and some of her eyebrows had re-appeared.

'Do you want me to do it, Aunty?' I volunteered, 'I know what to do, don't I Mam? I do it in our 'ouse, don't I?'

There was no refusal, so I carefully tore a thin strip off last night's *Echo*, folded it lengthwise twice, then managed to light it from the almost extinct embers in the grate. Climbing onto a chair, I pulled the chain to operate an elaborate lever and turn on the gas. The paper went out.

I jumped down from the chair and with some difficulty re-lit the paper. The gas refused to light and the paper went out again.

Third time lucky, the gas ignited.

'Woomph!' The lampshade exploded.

I fell off the chair and Arthur's mother screamed. Mam asked if I was all right and Arthur couldn't move for laughing. There were bits of glass everywhere, but most of it settled on Mrs Hughes' head. The slivers were sprinkled all over her hair, shimmering in the faint light, having failed to penetrate the permanent waves.

After a few minutes Mrs Hughes recovered some of her composure. 'That was a new shade that was,' she muttered accusingly, completing ignoring my struggle to regain consciousness. 'Now what am I going to do?'

My mother, somewhat thoughtlessly, announced that it was getting dark so we had better get home. She headed for the door before Mrs Hughes got round to exploring the possibility of compensation for the exploding lampshade. Mam was unlatching our back door before she remembered me. New shades cost 1*s*. 3*d*.; new hair and eyebrows cost nothing.

'Yoo-hoo Kenneth!' she shouted back across the jigger. 'Time to come in, it's getting dark an' mummy wants you to come in right away like a good boy and light the gas for me.'

My ears buzzed and my eyebrows were charred to little brown curls, but otherwise I was undamaged.

'Here's a big bit,' I handed a jagged piece of shade to Mrs Hughes. 'And there's some more bits on your 'ead.' I pointed to the slivers rocking to and fro on her perm. I had a vague idea that she could stick the pieces back together, so I began searching the floor for more fragments.

'You 'orrible cheeky little sod...'

I headed unsteadily but quickly through the dim light to the backyard and across the jigger to the safety of home.

'See you tomorrow, Arthur. Don't forget you're coming with me and me mam!' I shouted into the gloom. 'Don't forget, tomorrow!'

'What's a 'noculation?' Terry asked.

It was a few weeks before the exploding gaslight and the gang was sitting on heaps of broken bricks on the 'debbie' at the bottom of the street. Billy was idly throwing chunks of masonry at Hockaday's garage door, sometimes changing his aim as a pigeon came into range.

'You get needles stuck in you.' Billy aired his considerable knowledge of matters involving pain.

'What for?' Terry insisted, not convinced.

'Stops you gerrin' ill,' volunteered Georgie. 'It's a syringe thing and it stuffs stuff into your arm … like medicine … to stop you gerrin' ill.'

'You mean like if you break your leg like … you mean it stops you breakin' your leg?' Terry persisted.

'No, not like that kind of ill, the other kind … like, like,' Georgie struggled to think of an illness, 'like the Black Death,' he concluded. 'Nobody gets the Black Death anymore because of 'noculation.'

I began to get a bit worried. I had read a story about the Black Death – it wasn't very pleasant and nobody had stuck any syringes in me to stop me getting it.

'I 'aven't 'ad a 'noculation, 'ow about you Billy?' I asked.

Billy also looked a bit worried. 'I've norradit as well,' he looked accusingly at his brother. 'When were you done?' he demanded.

It was Georgie's turn to look worried. He knew from experience that Billy resented him getting anything that Billy didn't get too, and that Billy tended to even things up by thumping him.

Georgie had read the same story as me. I couldn't remember exactly what the tale was about, but it had something to do with a plague of rats led by the Pied Piper, biting people and wiping out half the population of London by the Black Death.

'No, I 'aven't 'ad it neither,' Georgie stated, hurriedly. 'I think they might 'ave 'noculated the rats and cured it,' he ended, lamely.

Further discussion was interrupted by the appearance of one of the less frequent members of the gang, who suffered torment from us because of his name: Dickie Balls.

Dickie's family was a bit more gentile than most in our street. They were determined to give Dickie the best possible start in life; so his parents tried their best to minimise his contact with us.

The Balls were the only coloured family in the street at the time, something of a novelty when they first arrived. The novelty soon wore off as Mrs Balls proved her expertise at gossiping with the best of the women, and Dickie joined our gang.

Dickie Ball's colour, however, did mean he got a special welcome when he managed to escape the eye of his mother and come out to play with us. ''Ow are your balls, Dickie?' we greeted him.

His chubby brown face beamed at the familiar welcome. 'Black and bigger than yours!' came the required reply. Having been welcomed in the traditional way, Dickie sat down on a pile of bricks. 'Me mam's takin' me to gerrinoculated tomorrow,' he announced mysteriously, waiting for the expected clamour of questions.

'Just as well.' Georgie tried to fight back laughter. 'Just as bloody well. You're the only bugger round 'ere who's gunner get Black Death!' He collapsed in a heap of hee-hawing laughter.

Dickie was nonplussed. 'What's he talkin' about? I'm getting inoculated against dip ... dip something or other; dip ... dip ... diphtheria, that's it, diphtheria, not Black Death.'

'What's diphtheria?' demanded Billy, always interested in adding to his knowledge of suffering.

'It's an illness, and gerrininoculated stops you gerrinit,' answered Dickie, again waiting for a barrage of questions.

'Oh we know all about 'noculation,' said Billy airily. 'It's what stopped the Black Death.' He turned accusingly to the still twitching body of Georgie. 'Thought you said rats gorrit, not people.'

Georgie thought fast. 'Depends on the type of illness,' He was beginning to enjoy his position as an authority on the subject. 'You 'noculate rats for Black Death and people for dipworreveritis.' This seemed to satisfy Billy.

''Ow do you catch this ... this dip thing?' Billy turned back to Dickie.

Dickie's mother had said it was something to do with lack of hygiene, whatever that was, and bad drains. He didn't want to appear ignorant; it was bad enough having different coloured skin. 'By drinking dirty drain water,' he stated, and ran off back home before he was asked why anyone would want to drink dirty drain water.

The next day we sought out Dickie, anxious to find out more about this mysterious inoculation. Dickie was on his way to our house, equally anxious to share his knowledge as a pioneer of the technique. He rolled up his shirt-sleeve as far as it would go, to expose a neat cross of sticking plaster.

'Black and bigger 'un yours,' he announced without waiting for the question, eager to get over the usual formalities of greeting. ''Noculation!' he pointed proudly at the plasters. 'Bloody great big needle right in there!'

We went quiet. Cuts and bruises, even the occasional broken bone, were one thing, needles were something different. I felt the colour in my face draining away. Georgie looked almost green.

Billy was made of sterner stuff. ''Ow big was it, and 'ow far did they stick it in?' he demanded. 'And 'ow many times?'

'About this big,' replied Dickie, proudly indicating a hypodermic needle the size of a bicycle pump. 'An' they stickirrin about two inches.'

I had a vague idea that two inches was thicker than his arm and nervously looked under his armpit for evidence of the needle coming out the other side.

'And they stickirrin about four times,' he continued, carried away by the effect his ordeal was having on Georgie and me. 'Burrit didn't bother me,' he added, nonchalantly pressing back a corner of the plaster.

'Your mam's taking Arthur an' me tomorrow,' said Terry faintly, turning to me. 'Tomorrow morning.' I said nothing. She was taking me as well.

Over the next few days kids from miles around were taken to a clinic in town and duly inoculated. I can't speak for the others, but supposed I must have been a special case, because all I felt was a slight prick from a tiny needle – once.

It was well worth going for the barley sugar sweet that the nurse handed out to the scruffy bawling queues of infants.

We each discussed our ordeal, with the size of needle and depth of penetration growing with each telling. But at least we had all survived the pain and none of us had cried; well, not much anyway.

More importantly, none of us had caught the Black Death, so 'noculation must work.

'How she can live with herself, I just do-not-know!' My mother continued the inquest outside our house that dusty sunny day, as I returned to the front door after emptying the pan of Tibby's fleas down the toilet. The same question was being asked by other groups of women on doorsteps up and down our street and the neighbouring streets.

Later that evening, my mother called me in from the street. She told me to sit down on the mat in front of the fireplace, because she had something very sad to tell me. She said she knew it would upset me, so if I didn't feel like going to school tomorrow, I could stay off.

It was almost dark when we sat down. For some reason or other, Mam had not lit the gaslight and, strangely, the black-leaded grate had no fire in it. The only light came from our tiny window, but it was enough to reflect the tears that glistened on my mother's cheeks.

I was used to her crying and sometimes sat on the landing outside her bedroom door while she sobbed inside, in the quietness that followed the shouting with Dad. I didn't cry then because I didn't understand the shouting and I couldn't see the tears. But her tears that night were shared with me, and so I cried too.

My mam sat on our old settee whilst I sat at her feet on the mat. She pulled me close to her. I knew my mother loved me and I loved her, but seldom did she show it, in the way she did that night. It must be hard to show love for someone, however much you feel it, if there is so much else not to love in your life.

That night she clung to me in the darkening room, quietly sobbing for a long time before she could speak. The small world of our familiar living room closed in on us until we were only aware of each other.

She told me that there was something called an epidemic in Liverpool. All of the mothers in the neighbourhood had been advised by the doctors, to take their children to be inoculated to keep them safe from an illness; an illness called diphtheria.

All the kids had been taken. All that is, except one.

And that one was her Little Arthur.

She told me that Little Arthur had become so ill that God had taken him to heaven. Her gentle voice fought the tears and I felt her despair as we sobbed together in the darkness of our little world. When at last she could cry no more and her despair became silent, she said I should go to bed and try to sleep.

It was so strange, this feeling of emptiness. Why was I crying?

I left my mother, her still form gently shaking as she sobbed in the darkness. It was only much later when I remembered that Mam was to have taken Arthur, with Terry and me, to the clinic.

Many years later my mother told me what had happened. It seems that when she went to collect Arthur to go to the clinic, Arthur's mother had said it didn't matter. Arthur was at the shops because she had to go out and have her hair done and wouldn't have time to do the shopping.

'Don't bother waiting for him, May,' she said to my mother. 'I'll take Arthur myself, as soon as I can. Now let me see, what am I doing tomorrow? Maybe I can take him then. Yes, I'll take him tomorrow.'

I knew nothing of death, but I knew all about heaven; they taught us all about it at Sunday School and it didn't sound a bad place to me, certainly not the sort of thing to cry about. But my mother had cried when she told me that her Little Arthur had been taken there, and so I had cried too.

That night in bed I lay awake, thinking about the games I used to play with Arthur and our competition to reach the top bolt on the back door. Sleep just would not come, so I got out of bed and knelt on the floor. I struggled to remember some of the prayers taught in morning assembly at school, but I couldn't. So I put my hands together like they said you should and I asked God about Arthur.

I asked him if Arthur could reach the latch on the golden gate that the Sunday School teacher said leads to heaven. And I asked him if there were any clockwork toys for Arthur to play with in heaven, because if there were

I would like the ones he had left behind in Ritson Street, because I was his best friend. And I asked him why Arthur had suddenly taken to drinking dirty drain water.

Then I told him that, because Arthur had died, I was having a day off school, and I asked God if he knew of anyone else in the street drinking dirty drain water and about to go to heaven. After all, another day off school was not to be sneezed at. But then tears welled in my eyes and I told God I would have to finish my prayers tomorrow.

Just then the bedroom door opened and Mam came in. 'Are you alright luv?' she asked. 'Do you think you can get to sleep?' Tears still glistened in her eyes.

I burst out crying. I cried for the first time in my life for someone other than myself. I cried for Arthur. I wanted Arthur to come and play out with me again. I wanted Arthur, not his toys. But most of all I wanted Arthur to know he was definitely the first to reach the bolt on our back door.

She came over, sat down and tucked me up tight in the bedclothes. 'Try to get some sleep,' she urged. 'You've got a busy day coming, playing out with Billy and Georgie.'

'Would Arthur be playing out if 'e'd been 'noculated?' I asked.

'Only God knows that,' said my mother, gently, 'and Arthur's with him now. He's in Heaven, so he won't be playing out in the street but I'm sure he'll be playing somewhere, tomorrow.'

Only todays mean anything when you are very young. There is only one today, but lots of tomorrows still to come. But that night as my mother sat on my bed, I cried myself to sleep and in my sleep I dreamt about tomorrows with Little Arthur.

I dreamt that Arthur was trying to reach the bolt on our back door before I did. I dreamt that I was going to the clinic with my mother to get inoculated. And I dreamt that she was going to bring her Little Arthur with us so that we wouldn't get ill.

We were all going to the clinic ... tomorrow.

A day at the seaside

'If our Billy's gone and drownded himself, I'll bloody-well kill him!'

Tis better to have loved and lost than never to have loved at all.

In Memoriam, Tennyson.

THE MURKY-BROWN WATERS of the River Mersey swirled and eddied around the massive timbers of the floating landing stage: churning, rushing, angry waters, backed upriver by estuary seas at flood tide.

Billy, his brother Georgie, Terry and I leaned against the safety chain stretched along the waterfront, exploring the broad expanse of the river, mesmerised by the scene before us. Billy and Georgie's mother stood behind us, fearful, or perhaps hopeful, that we might lean over too far.

We could just make out the structure of the Pier at New Brighton on the distant far side, with Seacome, Birkenhead and the shipyards of Cammell

FERRY ACROSS THE MERSEY

The ferry slowly swung away from the landing stage and headed off to midstream. The shuddering changed to a steady beat, speeding us on our way to New Brighton

Laird directly opposite, brisling with funnels and masts of new ships under build and rusting marine work-horses under repair.

The river itself was alive. A liner, perhaps bound for America as part of an Atlantic convoy, pushed the waters aside on its way to the Bar and the Irish Sea beyond, disdainful of the power of the tide. The Liverpool Pilot busily chaperoned the liner, showing the way to the Bar, bobbing and weaving in deference to the surging waters.

In midstream, a sand dredger clanked and groaned in its never-ending task of keeping the shipping lanes free of sandbanks constantly shifting under the Mersey's mighty tides.

Our view of the Liverpool side of the river was blocked: on one side by the broad beam of a moored tug, and on the other by the SS *Isle of Man*.

'See that ship there?' Terry pointed to the *Isle of Man*. 'That goes to an island that our Alan says is full of cats tharr'ave only got three legs and no bloody tail.'

We ignored him; cats like that were fairly common around Lodge Lane.

'Look at that!' Georgie nodded towards the far side of the river, directly opposite to us. The black hull and white superstructure of the *Royal Daffodil* was just leaving Birkenhead, the ferry's bow rising and plunging in the swell, ploughing the murky water into great plumes of milky-white spray. It was heading for Liverpool.

We watched with growing excitement as it neared its berth just a few yards from us. The steady 'thud-thud' of the engine stopped, then changed to a protesting judder, and the waters churned violently as its engines reversed to coax the ship alongside the landing stage.

A number of men in blue jerseys and black caps rushed out to catch lines hurled by the crew, pulling them and their following ropes, to loop them around massive cast-iron bollards, to capture the *Daffodil* and pull it tight against the enormous tyres hung along the stage.

Crowds of expectant passengers lined the rails, waiting impatiently as a section in the side of the boat slid sideways to accept the gangplank lowered from the stage, whilst those on the top deck were ushered out of the path of a smaller gangplank lowered from an elaborate crane-like structure. They surged from the ferry, hurrying up the tunnels from the floating stage to the solid earth of Liverpool, as though they had been at sea for months.

'Ey Mam, see these 'ere.' Billy walked over to one of the mooring bollards. 'See this rope, is this what they do on Lodgy?'

His mother was flabbergasted. Billy knew about something other than pain, death and methods of destruction. 'That's right, Billy! They made that at the rope works down by Bentley Street,' she was delighted at his interest.

'Is that where they make the ones as 'angs murderers, as well?' Billy stroked the heavy twists.

She didn't answer him; she didn't dare think of why he wanted to know.

Billy and Georgie's mother had reluctantly bent, under weeks of cajoling from her offspring, to take us on a treat to the Pier Head. She had this vague idea that it would be, somehow, instructional and that it might assist Tiber Street School's less than successful attempts at our education.

'Ey Mam, 'ow about takin' us on a ferry, next time?' Georgie watched the passengers bound for Birkenhead, boarding. 'It's only tu'pence return you know. 'Ow about it, Mam?'

'Go on, Mam, take us, it won't take long, we'll be back before tea, go on.' Billy supported his brother's plea, assuming his most grovelling voice, the one used to get us to the Pier Head.

'No, it's too late! We're going home now, and that's final!' Their mother had made the most elementary of mistakes: she hadn't refused point blank; she'd only said it was too late now.

'All right then, Mam, we don't wanner make you late, 'cause we know you're always busy, so we'll go on Sat'dy when you've done the shoppin'.' Billy's grovelling entreaty changed to statement of demand.

'We'll have to see,' his mother said, with a note of despair in her voice. 'Come on you lot, we're going home.' She led the way up the tunnel to the plateau in front of Cunard Building, and across to the tram terminus. We stood one behind the other in the queue for the No. 26.

Terry nudged Georgie and whispered to him. 'Do you think your mam'll gerrus an ice cream?'

A 'Stop me and Buy one' ice cream cart appeared from the road alongside the Liver Building, heading towards the landing stage.

'Ey, Mam, would you gerrus an ice cream please?' Georgie tugged the back of his mother's coat.

She raised her eyes to heaven. 'More money,' she muttered. 'Here you are then, small cornets mind you!' She took out her purse and handed him some copper.

'Can we 'ave raspberry juice on 'em?' Georgie pushed his luck.

'Not if it costs more!' she was adamant.

Georgie ran across to intercept the cart. The cart mounted the kerb onto the paved plateau. The second it left the cobbled road, its driver accelerated, pedalling as fast as he could, defying anyone to stop him and buy one.

There was simply no way Georgie was going to miss his cornet. He pelted straight at the cart, waving his arms. "Ey mister, I want four cornets!' he yelled. The driver's feet were a blur as he peddled furiously towards the tunnels, head down. 'Wiv raspberry on 'em, if it's free!'

The word 'free' must have caught his attention. The driver looked up to see Georgie standing in his path, about three yards away. He stopped pedalling and grabbed the brakes.

Most bikes in those days, particularly those powering 'Stop me and Buy one' carts, were fixed wheel; which meant if you stopped pedalling, the pedal took no notice and kept going, taking your feet with them, pushing you skywards.

The driver went up with pedals and the cart skidded to a stop, but the driver kept going. 'Arr! Oww!' He shot across the handlebar, landing face down amongst the cartons of ice cream.

'Can I 'ave four small cornets please, wiv raspberry on 'em, if it's free.' Georgie thrust his hand amongst the cartons to show the driver his money.

We couldn't quite hear what the driver said, but Georgie ran back to the tram queue empty handed. 'Christ, I only wanted an ice cream! An' that's what 'e's supposed to be sellin'. 'E wouldn't gimme one, Mam, an' you should 'ave 'eard worr'e called me. He called me a stupid...'

'If I ever hear you saying that again, I'll marmalise you. Go and wash your mouth out!' Georgie's mother tried to look horrified through the smile on her face. 'Serves you right he didn't sell any, now give me my money back!'

Further discussion was cut short by the arrival of the No. 26 for Lodge Lane.

'Who the hell's that banging on the door?' I was sitting alongside my mother on the settee, both of us reading. She was half way through A. J. Cronin's *Hatter's Castle*, and I was struggling with page one of *The Mystery of the Island*.

'I'll go an' gerrit.' It was a relief to give up the struggle. From now on, I'd stick with Enid Blyton. The words were shorter.

'You cummin' out, or what, Spud?' a hollow voice bellowed down the lobby, through the open letterbox.

I yanked open the door. Billy shot through the opening, still clinging to the open letterbox. 'Oww! Ooh-ooh, oww! Me bloody 'and!' Billy shook his hand to cool the pain.

It was a Friday evening, just after school, so he was dressed casually to play out. His feet were encased in black plimsoles with their rubber welt parting company from the canvas uppers, allowing one of the soles to flap open and expose a row of dirty toes. A grey, once white, singlet with a jam stain advertised what he had had for breakfast.

'These is me new braces, I gorrem from me Uncle Ron.' He slid his thumbs up and down behind the wide elastic straps, forcing his short black trousers to pull away from his waist, leaving a six-inch gap: evidence that his trousers probably came from the same source as his braces.

Georgie joined us. "Ave you told 'im yet, Billy?"

'No I 'aven't, so shurrup!' Billy turned round to threaten his brother.

"Ave a guess where we're goin' tomorrow.' He turned back to me. 'Go on, you can 'ave three guesses.'

'I give up.' Christ, it could be anywhere; I could be here all day, guessing. They both looked disappointed.

'Me mam says you can come as well, if you've got the money.' Georgie added.

At least the need for money narrowed the field. 'The pictures!' I tried one life.

'No, berrer than that!' they chorused.

'Woolton Woods!' Guess number two was bound to be right.

'No, berrer than even that! D'you give up?' Billy was enjoying himself. 'Go on. You'll never guess.'

'On the ferry!' It was my last life, but I knew I was right, I suddenly remembered their mother's inept handling of Billy's grovelling at the Pier-Head.

'Sort of.' Georgie agreed.

'Worra you mean, it's either a ferry, or it isn't. I was right, wasn' I?' I knew I was right, Georgie was just a bad loser.

'Yeh, we're goin' on a ferry all right, an' guess where we're goin' to.' Billy was dancing on the doorstep with excitement.

'I'm not guessin' any more, Christ, I'll be all day guessin'. Just tell me, or buggeroff.' It was the weekend, a chance to play out. I had no intention of spending it in mental torture, *The Mystery of the Island* was bad enough.

'Me mam's takin' us to New Brighton, and she says you an' Terry can come an' all, if you've got the money!' Billy grinned.

I knew there'd be a catch somewhere, there always was, and it usually involved money. 'When's she takin' us?' I asked.

'Tomorrer!' Billy replied.

'Mam!' I shouted back down the lobby. 'Mam, can I go to New Brighton with Billy's mam, tomorrow?'

'Yes, you can go, it's all agreed. Billy and Terry's mother are taking all of you.' Mother appeared at the kitchen door. 'And God help them,' she added, under her breath.

'We'll go and find Terry.' I banged the front door shut.

Terry was playing ollies in the gutter, outside Ocklershaw's shop, with Tommy. Billy ran up and jammed his foot in the gutter, blocking Tommy's marble as it careered towards Terry's six-hitter.

110

'What the sodden-'ell d'you think you're doin'?' Tommy was horrified. 'That would 'ave hit 'is, that would, an' I've already 'it it five times, so I was gunner win it for keeps this time, you silly bugger!'

We waited expectantly. Calling Billy a silly bugger was not to be recommended. Tommy's future was in doubt. Billy bent down, picked up both marbles, and handed them to Tommy. ''E would 'ave won it anyway, Terry.'

It was Terry's turn to be horrified. He bunched his fist. 'Gimme me ollie back, or else!' Billy and Tommy ignored him. Terry thought fast. 'Tell you what,' he said, 'me mam's takin' us all to New Brighton, tomorrer, all except you, Tommy. She didn' say anything about you, so you're not goin'; burrif you gimme me six-'itter back, you can come as well.'

The ollie was back in his hands before you could say Jack Robinson.

'Don't forget,' said Billy, 'me mam says you 'ave to be at our 'ouse at ten o'clock, so we can get the tram early.'

Half-past nine on Saturday, a lovely sunny day, saw us all leaning impatiently on Billy's railings. We were all dressed ready for the beach: pumps, no socks, open necked shirts, and carrying the standard implements for a hard day's play.

Between them, Georgie and Billy had managed to acquire a red painted spade with a broken handle, and an authentic if somewhat battered bucket: a tin bucket painted with a typical beach scene of children building an enormous sand castle, with a mounted donkey apparently intent on demolishing their work. Terry carried his leather case ball, and I had borrowed Charlie's cricket bat and ball. Tommy had done his best. Anything authentic was difficult to come by in Tommy's house, so he had been obliged to compromise: he carried a battered copper jelly mould, by way of a bucket, and a big wooden ladle, by way of a spade.

We were well equipped and raring to go.

'We're ready, Mam!' Georgie shouted through the open door.

'We'll go just as soon as Terry's mother comes, so shurrup or you won't go at all!' she replied.

Ten minutes later, Terry's mother arrived. The two women took no notice of us, but chattered away to each other as they walked up Tagus Street to the tram stop on Lodge Lane. We followed our chaperones, marching in step to the beat of spades on buckets and ladles on jelly moulds. The two women looked at each other, raised their eyes to heaven, and prayed for a swift end to the day.

A No. 27 arrived almost immediately. The two mothers, with Terry, went along the lower deck, looking for a seat, but it was full. The rest of us charged past the conductor and threw ourselves up the stairs to the top deck.

'Go upstairs, Terry, and see if you can get us a seat. I don't want to have to stand all the way to town, I'm getting too old for that.'

Terry joined us. The top deck was almost full, but there was one seat left on a bench for two, the adjacent seat and half the ally-way being occupied by a large middle-aged woman. Terry strode up to the empty seat and addressed the large woman. ''Scuse me, missus, can we 'ave your seat please, 'cause we 'ave to 'ave it for these old women who's takin' us to the seaside.'

The large lady smiled at him. 'Well of course you can, young man; how very thoughtful of you.' She struggled out of her seat, helped by Billy, and stood aside in the aisle. Our chaperones clattered up the stairs in their high-heels, skipped sideways along the aisle and sat down.

'You lying little sod!' The large woman elbowed Billy out of the way and leaned over the seat, her bulk almost enveloping the two young mothers.

'Gerrup out-a me seat! I'll 'ave you thrown off, I will, pretending to be old. Cheeky buggers.' Her face was blotchy-red with fury. 'Should be bloody-well ashamed of 'emselves.' She addressed the rows of passengers.

Our chaperones were bright red with embarrassment, uncomprehending, but suspicious that whatever it was they had done to upset the large woman had something to do with Terry. They got up, forced their way past the mass of their tormentor, and went back downstairs.

The conductor arrived on the top deck and made straight for us. He was well versed in the technique of kids keeping out the way until they got to where they were going, then disembarking without paying whilst the tram was still in motion.

'Fares, please.' It was more of a threat than a request.

'No, mister, we're not payin,' Terry advised. The conductor drew himself to his full height, ready for battle. Terry hurriedly continued, 'No, we don' 'ave to, mister, me mam's down stairs, she's payin'.'

The conductor backed along the aisle and down the stairs, making sure there was no escape for us. 'Who's paying for those hooligans up stairs?' he demanded.

The two mothers instantly recognised the description. 'We are,' they chorused.

'Two adults, and four children to the Pier Head, please.' Terry's mother tipped some coins from her purse.

'There's five of 'em up there,' the conductor replied, belligerently.

'Well only four of them's ours, and four of them is quite enough, thank you,' she smiled sweetly, 'you can have the other one if you like,' she giggled.

'There's five of 'em as says they're with you, so you're payin' for five or I'm chucking the 'ole lot of you off.'

By this time, the lower deck were beginning to question the honesty and morals of our chaperones: what kind of mother would disown her own child to save a penny fare? The upper deck had already made their minds up.

The whole lower deck fixed our minders with looks varying from mild disapproval from those who had had serious thoughts about disowning their own children, to horror from the more maternal amongst them.

They both went bright red with embarrassment.

We were nearing the Pier Head, so we trooped downstairs, lead by Terry. Terry's mother counted us: Terry-one, Billy-two, Georgie-three, me-four, Tommy-five. Tommy! Where the hell did he come from?

'What are you doing here?' Terry's mother confronted Tommy.

'I'm wiv you, missus, you're takin' me to New Brighton.'

The women were crimson with embarrassment.

'But we weren't taking you!' She tried to recover some dignity by way of explaining why she was only paying for four of us.

'Ought to be ashamed of yourself!' The large lady had followed us down. 'First they pinch me seat, then they try to pretend their own little boy doesn't belong to 'em, then they won't take 'im to the seaside with his brothers, an' 'e looks 'alf starved to me. Y'ought to be bloody-well ashamed of yourselves you should!'

The tram pulled up at the terminus. Terry's mother threw the nine-pence fare at the conductor and leapt off the tram, running as fast as she could for the landing stage, followed hot on her heels by Billy's mother.

'Look at 'em now, they're runnin' away from their own children!' The large lady's voice pursued them across the Pier Head.

We joined them at the New Brighton boarding station, under the green cast-iron gantry that controlled the ferry's upper deck boarding platform.

'What are you doing here?' Terry's mother glared at Tommy. Tommy stood before her, his mouth open, nervously banging his ladle against the jelly mould.

'It's all right, Mam, I said 'e could come, 'cause 'e gave me me six-'itter back,' Terry explained.

'Oh, you did, did you! Do you know what trouble you've caused! Do you...' She gave up, frustrated. She knew she wouldn't get away with infanticide; the large woman on the tram would see to that.

She turned to Tommy. 'And I don't suppose you've got any money, either?'

'No, missus, 'cause your Terry didn't say I'd 'ave to bring any, 'cause I gave 'im 'is six-'itter back.'

'Oh, sodden-'ell, come on then.' The women looked at each other again, then to heaven. Whoever was up there was not listening. It had been a long hard day already, and it was only five-past eleven in the morning.

The river waters were flat calm on an ebbing tide. Small boats and ferries busied to and fro, weaving between moored liners, and warships. We could just make out the New Brighton ferry *Egremont*, more than half way across the river.

At long last it crunched against the tyres of the landing stage and began disgorging its passengers. We fought our way through the stragglers, up the steps of the gantry and onto the top deck of the ferry, with our minders following.

''Ere y'are, Mam, sit 'ere.' Terry threw himself onto one of the slatted wooden seats. We sat on one side of the bench, separated from the mothers by its high back.

The ferry was soon packed with day-trippers: mams and a few dads, grandmothers and grandfathers, and hundreds of children clutching buckets and spades, laughing and shouting and singing. They thronged the rails, shouting for stragglers to hurry up, then exhorting the crew to start the engines and get going.

'Can we go an' 'ave a look at the water, please?' Billy kneeled up on his seat and leaned over the back, frightening the life out of his mother, who had just closed her eyes to take in the sea air.

'Don't do that, for Christ's sake. Let's have a bit of peace before we get there.'

Billy took this to mean we could go. We ran along the length of the boat, and hung over the rail at the side of the ferry, near the stern. Suddenly, the deck began to shudder and grumble under our feet. Smoke billowed from the funnel and the water churned below us. The *Egremont* slowly swung away from the landing stage and headed off to midstream. The shuddering changed to a rhythmic 'thud-thud' as the engines settled to a steady beat, speeding us on our way to New Brighton.

We ran to the front of the ferry and climbed on the rails to feel and smell the sea breeze. Seacombe and Birkenhead glided past, Cammell Laird disappeared behind us, and slowly the Pier at New Brighton began to dominate the waterfront on the opposite side of the river to Liverpool.

'Let's go an' 'ave a look around the ship,' said Terry, heading for the stairs to the lower deck.

The stairway was full of sitting people, unable to find anywhere else to sit. We picked our way down, then through the tangle of bicycles propped against each other near the entrance to the covered lounges, and made our way to the stern, to find Billy staring at a 'No admittance' sign. The sign invited us to climb over the chains barring our way, onto a raised platform. Billy climbed onto the platform and then to the top of the safety rail.

'Aww, you should see this!' He craned his neck, peering down. The water boiled as the propellers thrust the ferry down-river. 'You can see the engine, 'ere, come an' 'ave a look!' Billy invited us to join him.

'I'm goin' back to me mam, we'll be there soon,' Georgie declined the offer, ''an you'd better come an' all, you're not supposed to be on there.'

We left Billy, and went back upstairs. New Brighton was only a few minutes away.

'Where's Billy? We'll be there in a minute,' his mother shouted to Georgie.

'He's lookin' over the back of the ship, Mam, an' I told 'im to come back, 'cause it says you shouldn't go where 'e's gone.'

Their mother sat bolt upright. 'Oh my God! What d'you mean! Where is he!' She looked panic-stricken. She grabbed Georgie by the shoulder. 'Show me where he is!'

Georgie was delighted. It was obvious from her tone that Billy had done something he shouldn't have done, and was in deep trouble. 'This way, Mam,' he ran ahead, anxious to be in the front line when punishment was metered out. His mother clattered after him, running as fast as her high heels would allow.

Georgie skidded to a halt in front of the 'No admittance' sign. There was not a sight nor sound of Billy. All you could hear was the churning of the ship's propeller. 'Where is he? Oh my God, where is he?' his mother shrieked in anguish.

Georgie climbed over the rail to look over the stern. ''E's not down 'ere, Mam,' he shouted, helpfully.

The colour drained from her face and, before Terry's mother could stop her, she climbed over the safety rail and joined Georgie, peering over the back of the ferry at the foaming water.

'Wonder worrappened to 'im?' Georgie scanned the horizon.

Tears streamed down his mother's face. 'Tell 'em to stop the ship, my Billy's fallen overboard! Oh my God, Billy's fallen overboard!'

'It's all right, Mam.' Georgie turned to look at her, surprised at the tears. 'It's all right, Billy can swim, 'e's just gorris twenny-five yards swimmin' certificate from school.'

His mother was near to panic. 'Stop the ship, someone stop the ship!' she screamed.

Terry's mother tried to take charge of the tragedy. 'Come back over here and we'll see what we can do.' She couldn't make up her mind whether the loss of Billy was a tragedy or a Godsend.

Her plea seemed to calm the stricken mother. She climbed back to safety and took hold of Terry's mother's hand. 'If our Billy's gone and drownded himself, I'll bloody-well kill him!' she said, tearfully.

'I'm sure that's that woman who was on the tram, the one as tried to get away without paying for her little boy, an' who tried to runaway from him when she got off.' A number of passengers had gathered at the scene of the tragedy, and one of them was pointing at Billy's mother.

We all stood in a row, with a small crowd behind us, studying the foaming wake of the ferry, trying to catch a glimpse of Billy before he went down for the third time.

'Worrare you lookin'at?' Billy pushed in, between his mother and me.

His mother stared fixedly out to sea. 'Our Billy, we're looking for our Billy, he's fallen into the sea,' she sobbed.

Billy climbed onto the top rail and put his hand over his eyes to shield them from the sun, anxious to witness the death throws of whoever had fallen overboard. 'I can't see no one, Mam,' he said, disappointed.

'It's our Billy,' she sobbed, 'it's our Billy, our poor Billy's fallen in … it's our … it's … it's … it's you! You haven't fallen in! Oh, thank God, you're safe!' She threw her arms around the resurrection, clinging to him until she was convinced it was Billy, safe from the clutches of Davy Jones and his Locker.

'No Mam, I 'aven't fallen in, an' even if I 'ad 'ave done, I'd 'ave been all right, I've got me swimmin' certificate,' he grinned.

'You bloody little sod! You frightened the bloody life out of me, you did! Where have you been, we thought you'd fallen in the water!' Relief had turned to anger; she even sounded a bit disappointed.

'I only went to 'ave a look at where the driver sits, Mam. Billy protested.

'You bloody little get, you just wait till I get you home! I was worried sick you'd drownded, I'm going to bloody-well kill you stone dead when we get home!' She aimed a slap at Billy's rear end, but missed.

'Look at her! She's got her little boy back an' now she's gunner batter 'im! She didn' want him back, if you ask me!' The woman from the tram turned to her neighbours in the crowd who, somewhat disappointed at the outcome of the drama, were beginning to drift away. 'She ought to be reported, she should.'

Nobody was listening, the crowd had lost interest: drownings were fairly unusual on the New Brighton ferry, but women battering their offspring was a common sight.

Georgie smiled to himself. It was going to be a wonderful day at the seaside, and the icing on the pudding would be the demise of Billy when they got home.

We returned to the upper deck as the boat began to slow down. The

LANDING STAGE

*We joined them at the New Brighton boarding station, under the green cast-iron gantry
that controlled the ferry's upper deck boarding platform*

passengers cheered and jostled for quick disembarkation as the ferry shud-
dered to a reluctant stop against the geometric tangle of cast ironwork of
the New Brighton Pier.

The first few off leapt onto the end of the still descending gangplank
then ran up the tunnel to the pay-desks, followed by hordes of the less
daring.

'Two adults and four children's returns please.' Billy's mother handed
over a pile of coins.

We piled through the turnstile.

'Where d'you fink you're goin'!' The official in a black peaked cap leaned
over his counter and grabbed Billy.

'I'm wiv me mam, she's just paid.' Billy protested.

'Not for you, she 'asn't! She only paid for four kids, and four 'ave gone
through!'

'Sodden-'ell, she doin' it again!' The woman from the tram arrived at the turnstile. 'That's 'is mother up there.' She pointed out Billy's fast disappearing mother to the official. 'She's been trying to get rid of the poor little thing all day, she has. First she tried to run away from him when she got off the tram, then she tried to throw him overboard from the ferry, now she's running away from him again.' She shook her head. What was the world coming to?

'Where's he gone again?' Our minders stopped at the top of the tunnel.

The man behind the turnstile roared at them. ''Ey you! There's a law about runnin' away from your kids! Come an' gerrim, or else!'

'Oh my God! I've done it again! I keep forgetting there's five of them; I keep forgetting Tommy's with us!' Billy's mother fumbled in her handbag, found tu'pence and handed the coins to me. 'Go back and pay for Billy, luv.'

I raced back to the turnstile and handed over the fare. 'She keeps forgerrin there's five of us,' I advised the official.

''Ow the 'ell can you forget you've got five sodden kids? I dunno what's wrong wiv women nowadays. I dunno...' Further words failed him and he handed me the ticket.

Rejoining the others, we became immersed in the crowd, carried along towards the exit, jostling and chattering excitedly, to spill out of the tunnel alongside the entrance arch of the Pier. We were all dazzled by our sudden return to sunlight and by the noise and sights around us, by the smell of salty air, ice creams and fish and chips. Cockle and candy-floss stands vied for space amongst roundabouts of brightly painted cars and fire engines, plywood trams and smiling cockerels full of laughing, screaming and sometimes terrified children.

Gaudily decorated stalls lined the railings all along the Pier, buntings rustling in a gentle breeze, with extravagant signs inviting the onlookers to 'Stick an ace and win a prize!' using three darts with hardly a flight between them. Others exhorted us to 'Catch a duck and win a goldfish'. Little girls, balanced horizontally across the barrier, tried desperately to catch yellow painted ducks circling in a tiny pond, with a hook on a stick. Red faced and tearful, they gave up after their three goes yielded only ducks with 'lost' painted on their bottoms, leaving the goldfish to die of old age, or perhaps starvation, in their tiny glass bowls stacked on shelves at the back of the stall.

The Pier thrust its way across the sands, out into the Mersey, dissecting the long ribbon of beach packed with day-trippers. There was hardly an inch between spread-eagled sunbathers with handkerchiefs or caps on their heads, sometimes both, and most with their boots on, children furiously digging, flinging sand wherever it landed, batters and bowlers, picnics, and elderly folk queuing for pots of tea at stalls propped against the sea wall.

Dozens more paddled, crying out with feigned terror as a misjudged wave lapped higher than their rolled-up trousers, or hitched skirts. Children tightly clasped their mothers' hands and bravely danced the surf, screaming in real terror when they tripped and ended up face down in the silt-laden water.

It was wonderful: the sights, the sounds, the smells of the seaside.

Georgie tugged at his mother's coat. ''Ey Mam, can we 'ave a go on that?' He pointed to the 'Caterpillar' as it rumbled to a stop on its wavy track. 'It's only a penny a go.' The green canvas tube folded back to disgorge its fraught passengers, all laughing and shouting, but secretly vowing never again.

'No you can't! That's not for children, it goes too fast,' she replied.

'Well worrabout that one, then?' He redirected his mother's attention to a more sedate roundabout of circling horses.

'We'll see in a minute,' She answered.

Billy was aghast. 'I don't wanner go on that! That's only for sodden kids; I wanner go on that one there.' He pointed to the fairground across the road, opposite the Pier. A purple and gold 'Waltzer' hurtled round, coaches spinning on their axis, rising, dropping, bouncing, in its mad career around the track.

'I'm dying for a cup-a tea,' Billy's mother hurriedly changed the subject and set off down the slip-way, onto the beach. 'Right you lot, take your shoes off so they don't get ruined by the sand, and sit down there while I get something to drink, and don't move till we get back.'

'I'll 'ave a big lemonade,' Billy staked his claim.

'You'll have what you're given! Now sit down and don't move, I don't want you getting lost.'

We sat down against the sea wall, took off our shoes and tied the laces together, to hang them around our necks.

Tommy began to ladle sand into his jelly mould. 'It's too bloody soft, look, it won't stay up!' He inverted the mould and expertly tapped the bottom. The mound of sand collapsed.

'It's gorrer be wet, you thick or something?' Billy said, helpfully. 'You 'ave to gerrit from by the sea.' With that, he picked up the jelly mould and headed to the water's edge.

'Me mam'll kill you, she will; you're supposed to stay 'ere.' Georgie's reminder was lost in the shouting, laughing of thousands.

Billy strolled along the water's edge until he found a space between paddlers, scooped a mould full of sand and upturned it. The sculpture was perfect: domed and ribbed, with the shape of a rabbit on top. He was so intent on his task that he failed to notice arrival of a small group of boys.

119

'What's that supposed to be?' A tall, slim, well-dressed youth examined the jelly mould. They all carried large tin buckets painted with scenes of the seaside, and brand new spades. 'You're supposed to have a bucket and a spade, not whatever that is,' the tallest boy, sporting white shorts and a striped short-sleeved shirt, addressed Billy.

Billy could hardly understand a word he said: none of it was Scouse.

'Buggeroff.' Billy covered all possible interpretations.

'What did you say?' the youth was obviously having some difficulty with Billy's diction. Billy ignored him and produced another perfect rabbit sculpture. 'Do you know what?' the youth turned to his friends, 'I believe he's using a jelly mould!' His friends laughed. 'Why don't you use a proper bucket?' he turned back to Billy.

'Buggeroff!' Billy produced another rabbit.

'You swore at me, you did!' The youth, a good six inches taller than Billy, was obviously appalled at Billy's language. 'That'll teach you!' He aimed a kick at the third rabbit. Billy watched the sculpture disintegrate.

The youth took his silence as submission. He kicked away rabbit number two. Billy watched in silence as it flew apart.

Billy stood silently as the youth lifted his foot for the third time, then, without a word, launched himself at his tormentor, feet flaying, sandy fists swinging.

The youth went down under the onslaught, watched in amazement by his friends. Billy pummelled the white shorts and striped shirt, pausing only to pick up his ladle and jelly mould to augment his fists and feet. The rest of the boys ran off to advise their parents of the imminent demise of their friend.

After a couple more bangs on the head with the jelly mould, Billy finally spoke. 'If you say 'barley' an' gimme your bucket an' spade, I'll let ye go!'

'Barley,' the youth whispered through swollen lips. Billy picked up the bucket and spade, and began to practise making sandcastles with his newly acquired professional tools.

'Where's Billy?' Our minders had returned with a pot of tea, a large jug of lemonade and four cups.

'Mind you don't break any of these.' Terry's mother set the pot and cups down on the sand. 'There's sixpence deposit on them.'

'Where's Billy?' His mother repeated, a note of anxiety creeping into her voice.

''E's gone down to the water; I told 'im not to go,' Georgie answered, piously. 'I told 'im you'd batter 'im when 'e got back,' he added, hopefully. Billy's mother anxiously scanned the milling hordes at the water's edge.

NEW BRIGHTON
BEACH

*There was hardly an
inch between spread-
eagled sunbathers with
handkerchiefs or caps on
their heads, sometimes
both...children furiously
digging...and elderly folk
queuing for pots of tea at
stalls propped against the
sea wall*

There was no sign of Billy. 'P'raps 'e's gone for a swim,' Georgie suggested, ''e might be practisin' 'is twenny-five yards.'

'Billy!' his mother screamed and ran down the beach as fast as her high heels would let her. She pushed her way through the paddlers and castle makers. 'Billy! Billy! Where are you Billy? If you've gone in the water, I'll sodden-well kill you! Billy luv, where are you luv? Come here or I'll bloody-well marmalise you!'

Billy, surrounded by a dozen or more sand castles, heard his name, and the tone in his mother's voice. He was just about to run back to where he was supposed to be, when he was confronted by the well-dressed boys, supported by a number of equally well dressed adults.

'That's him, father!' the taller youth pointed to Billy from behind his father's back.

'Come here you little ruffian!' the father grabbed Billy by the arm.

'Lemme go, I 'aven't done nothin', 'e was makin' fun of me bucket!' Billy protested, struggling to break the grip on his arm. A small crowd gathered. It was obvious that some form of violence was about to happen.

Billy's mother spotted the gathering. Some instinct, or perhaps long experience, told her that the expectant crowd might have something to do with Billy. She pushed her way through to the front row.

'I'm going to box your ears for what you did! You assaulted my little boy, you did, you dreadful creature,' the youth's father glared at Billy.

'That's my Billy you've gorrold of!' Billy had his back to his mother, but reference to a dreadful creature told her it must be her son.

'It is, is it, madam? Well let me tell you that he is a hooligan and a thief! He hit my son and kicked him, and...'

'You just let go of him, or else!' Billy's mother interrupted him and wrenched her son free. She was happy to accept her son being described as a hooligan, and was well aware of Billy's penchant for violence against the person; but he was not a thief. Family honour was at stake.

'How dare you call my Billy a thief! I'll have the law on you, I will! Come on Billy luv, you just forget about the horrible man and come with your mummy.' She took Billy by the hand, threaded her way through the disappointed onlookers and led him back to the rest of us.

'Do you know what that man said about our Billy?' She sat down on the sand alongside Terry's mother, her face white with anger. 'He called him a thief! A thief, our Billy a thief!'

Terry's mother muttered something by way of sympathy, wondering what all the fuss was about. Everybody knew Billy was a budding psychopath, so a bit of thieving as a sideline was hardly a big deal.

'That's one thing our Billy isn't, he's not a thief, are you Billy, luv?' she turned to her son.

Billy didn't hear her; he was talking to Tommy. ''Ere y'are, Tommy, you can chuck that jelly thing away now, you can 'ave this, it's a real one.' He handed Tommy the recently acquired brand-new bucket.

His mother stared blankly at the offering, frightened to ask the question.

Tommy took the bucket, turning it round and round, admiring the pictures painted on it. 'Cor, look at that! Cor, that's smashing tharris. Aww, thanks Billy, where did you gerrit?' he asked Billy's mother's question for her.

'Made that feller gimme it. Told 'im I'd batter 'is bloody 'ead off if 'e didn' gimme it,' Billy smiled, proudly.

'Oh my good God!' his mother buried her head in her hands. Not only was Billy a thief, he was guilty of robbery with violence.

She struggled to her feet, desperate for some form of salvation. She scanned the edge of the water looking for the victim of her son's violent theft, but he was nowhere in sight. Even confession of her family's sins was denied to her.

Terry' mother adopted a more pragmatic approach. 'Don't worry about it, it's a lovely bucket, it must have cost a fortune. Have another cup of tea, and you'll be all right, you'll see.' Billy's mother took the offered cup. Staring unseeingly into the distance, she prayed again for the end of the day.

'Can we go for a paddle, Mam?' Georgie stood up, and taking silence as a 'yes', he headed for the water. We all followed.

''Ey, look, 'ere's a crab!' Terry scrambled out of the water. 'Bloody big 'un. They can bite your toe off, you know!'

Billy waded in. 'Where is it, I can't see the bugger!' he thrashed around with his spade, stirring up the silt. 'There it is!' He stooped down, urging the crab into his bucket. 'Got you, you bugger!' We all peered into the bucket. The crab circled the rim, menacing us with outstretched claws. 'Look at the size of 'im, 'e'd 'ave your finger off in no time, 'e would.' Billy waded back out.

A small group of little girls saw us peering into the bucket. 'What 'ave you got in there?' A red-headed girl, cheekier than her friends, pushed between us. 'Cor, you aren't 'alf brave, you are. 'Ey, look, 'e's caught a crab.' She encouraged her friends to have a look. They crowded round excitedly.

'Did you catch him all by yourself then?' the red-head asked.

'Course I did.' Billy was enjoying his position as big-game hunter. 'I'm not frightened of a sodden crab, I caught it wiv me 'ands,' he added.

'Let's see you pick 'im up then.' The little girl's freckled face was a picture of innocence.

Billy blanched.

'Go on then, pick 'im up,' she insisted, 'if you're not frightened, pick 'im up.'

We all waited expectantly as Billy stared at the circling crab.

'You didn't catch it all by yourself, did you?' She turned to her friends. 'He's tellin' fibs, he is. He's frightened of it. You're frightened of it, you are,' she turned back to Billy.

'I'm not sodden-well frightened of it! I did catch it by meself, honest. I just don't wanner kill it by takin' 'im out of the water.'

'They can live out of water, crabs can.' A girl with pig-tails, in a gingham dress, gave Billy the benefit of her knowledge of shellfish. 'So you can take it out, and it won't do it no harm.'

Billy's status as big-game hunter was in jeopardy. He poked the crab's claw, quickly withdrawing his hand. The crab ignored him, continuing its search for an escape route. Reassured, he took hold of a claw and hauled the crab out of the bucket.

''Ere y'are, told you I wasn't frightened.' Billy thrust the crab towards the girls. They screamed and hid behind us.

The crab couldn't believe its luck. Free from the bucket, the only thing between it and its home in the sea was Billy's hold on one of its claws. It made a couple of tentative jabs at his fingers with its free claw, found they were made of flesh and blood, and took a firm hold.

It was Billy's turn to scream. 'Ow! Ow! It's bitin' me bloody 'and off! Ow! Ow! Gerrit off me, gerrit off me 'and!' He let go of the claw and shook his

123

hand, more in fear of the unknown than in pain. Satisfied it was free, the crab let go and sailed through the air to hit the little red-head on the chest.

She screamed in terror, the little girl with pig-tales joined her, and soon the whole group was shrieking in fear for their lives.

The crab picked its way unhurriedly across the sand and into the sea

The little girls' parents had been watching their offspring with increasing anxiety, as Billy's more or less innocent bravado turned to panic accompanied by language not fit for little girls.

'You foul-mouthed hooligan! What are you doing, frightening little girls!' One of their fathers came up behind Billy and gripped him by the ear. Billy screamed. He thought it was a giant crab intent on revenge.

'I think your Billy's in trouble again.' Terry's mother jabbed her friend who was still staring unseeingly into the distance. 'He's down by the water, and some man's telling him off,' she advised.

Still with her eyes fixed on the horizon, and without saying a word, Billy's mother walked slowly down the beach. The little girl's father was still berating Billy, advising him on the state of his mind and the misuse of the English language. His mother pushed through the group surrounding Billy, took hold of his free ear and, still without saying a word, pulled.

'Ow! Ow! You're pullin' me ears off! Ow! Ow! Let go of me ears, you're pullin' me 'ead off!'

The shock of a mute women suddenly gripping the other side of the hooligan's head caused the little girl's father to let go. Billy was dragged sideways up the beach by his mother, crab-fashion, accompanied by the little girl's father's advice. 'Should be locked up, he should. Foul mouthed hooligan, frightening the life out of little girls, foul mouthed bully!'

Billy was dumped against the wall and his mother returned to studying the horizon.

'Can we go for a paddle under the pier, Mam?' Terry was getting bored, burying his feet in the sand. 'We'll make sure Billy be'aves 'imself.'

'I'll come with you and make sure he does,' Terry's mother struggled to her feet. 'You have some more tea, dear, we won't be long.' She poured the tepid remains from the teapot and handed it to her silent friend.

We dodged our way through the half-naked bodies and ran along the water's edge to the pier. The cast iron pillars, coated with slimy dripping seaweed and clusters of pearly-black mussels, seemed to close in on us as I led the way under the pier. Sunlight disappeared, replaced by an eerie gloom, as the chattering laughter of the beach changed to a dull rumbling echo of hundreds of feet tramping the boardwalk overhead. We fell silent, a little afraid of the dank gloom.

'Now you lot be careful; I'm staying here to get a bit of a tan.' Terry's mother sat down on the sand, leaned her head back and closed her eyes from the glare of the sunlight.

We crept along, ankle deep in water, into the twilight. 'Drip, plop-plop, drip': water dripped from the boards and the criss-crossed girders.

Tommy stopped at one of the cast iron supports. 'See this 'ere. See this, you can make 'em pop.' He pulled a frond of slimy bladder-wort from the encrusted iron-work. ''Ere y'are, look.' Tommy popped a flotation bulb on the weed between his fingers. 'Great, innit?' The bulb popped with a satisfying 'plop', releasing a squirt of water.

'Let's 'ave a go!' Billy grabbed a long length of weed and, not content with Tommy's one-at-a-time approach, laid it on a flat rock and jumped on it. Slimy weed and wet rocks are not the most sensible things to jump on. 'Aaar! Sodden-'ell!' Billy slipped and ended up sprawled full length in muddy water. 'Sodden-'ell, I'm soaking wet!'

Georgie carefully stepped over him. 'Me mam'll batter you when you get 'ome, she will.' He picked up Billy's weed and began popping the bulbs.

Ten minutes or so later, we were becoming bored with popping seaweed.

'Ey, look at this! Worrisit?' Tommy knelt down, poking at the sand with his spade. We joined him. A translucent lump of off-white jelly with a purple centre lay in the sand. A few feet away, several other lumps lay scattered on the sand.

'Blimey! That's a jellyfish that is!' Georgie prodded the lump. 'It's dead, it's not movin'.'

'Worrever you do, don't touch it!' I warned, 'it mightn't be dead, it might be asleep or just pretending to be dead, just waitin' for someone to touch it an' then it'll sting 'em an' kill 'em.'

Tommy jumped back a couple of feet and dropped his spade.

'Bloody coward, course it's dead. What d'you think it's doin' on the sand. If it was alive it'd be floatin' about in the water.' Tommy picked up the spade and poked the jellyfish. 'Look, course it's dead. It's not movin' is it?' He turned it over. The lump showed no sign of life.

Billy, anxious to re-establish his reputation as a hunter, bent down and tried to pick it up. The rotting mass of jelly slithered out from between his fingers. 'Sodden-'ell, it stinks!' He gasped at the putrid smell.

''Ere y'are, let me 'ave a go,' Tommy used the spade to manoeuvre the lump into Billy's cupped hands.

'I gunner show it to me mam.' Billy thought that if he showed some interest other than getting soaking wet, beating up boys and frightening little girls, his mother might show him some mercy when he got home.

Tommy led the way back out from under the pier into the sunlight and up the beach, followed by Georgie, Terry and me, with Billy last, carefully shuffling the stinking mass to keep it in his upturned palms. We filed our way between sunbathing bodies, games of cricket and sandcastles, with Billy concentrating on the unstable dollop of jellyfish.

'Sodden-'ell! Ow!' Billy stepped into the moat of an elaborate sandcastle and fell down on his knees. The jelly swayed then slowly slithered out of his outstretched hands. He clawed at the rotting mass, trying desperately to keep a grip, but it seemed to have a life of its own. It slipped from his hands, landing with a faint 'plop' on the rounded stomach of the owner of the sandcastle, fast asleep alongside his creation.

'Aaar! Oooh! What the sodden-hell!' The sandcastle builder screamed and shot bolt upright, clawing at the alien presence on his stomach, so suddenly that he fell over onto his castle. The jelly slid down his stomach like something from a horror film. 'Ooh! Gerri-off me. Warrisit! Warrisit!' He tried to get to his feet to flee from the horror, tripped over the castle and landed on top of the nightmare. 'Aaar! Gerri-off, gerri-off!'

Billy got to his feet. 'It's all right mister, it's only a jellyfish, an' it's dead so it won't do you no 'arm. Can I 'ave it back please, so I can show me mam.'

The man stopped thrashing around and recovered some of his composure. He took the handkerchief off his head, and wiped his rounded stomach. 'You bloody little 'ooligan! It stinks that does! What's wrong wiv you, carryin' dead jellyfish all over the place. Christ there's something wrong wiv you, there is. An' look what you've done to me castle! You've ruined it you 'ave, an' it took me hours to do it, you stupid little 'ooligan.'

'I didn' mean it mister, honest, an I only done in part of it. You buggered up the rest when you fell on it.'

'You cheeky sod. I'll batter your bloody 'ead in, in a minute. Now sod off, or else!'

Terry's mother witnessed the whole episode, but kept her distance, before making her way back to the seawall. 'I think you'd better go and get your Billy again. He's thrown a dead jellyfish at this man, then ruined his sandcastle. You'd better go and get him before the man does.'

Still gazing into the distance, Billy's mother sighed, then, without a word, made her way along the beach to rescue Billy.

Another cup of tea waited her return.

We all sat down with our backs to the wall, a patch of wet sand slowly growing around Billy.

'Right, you can have your sandwiches now.' Terry's mother took a big parcel of greaseproof paper out of her shopping bag. 'One at a time, one at a time!' She slapped Tommy's handful of sandwiches.

Billy leaned over, took the biggest round of bread from the bottom and upended the heap of egg butties, tipping them onto the sand. His mother leaned over and, still silent, heaped them back onto the paper, covered in sand.

We worked our way through the heap, spitting out tongue-fulls of sand, washing the rest down with gulps of lemonade. Our minders sipped another cup of tea.

'Terry, take the teapot and things back, and get the six-pence deposit; then we'll go and have a look at the fair.'

Before Terry could get to his feet, Billy jumped up, anxious to make amends. 'I'll take 'em, Mam, I'll get the deposit.' He balanced the cups and jug on the teapot and headed for the refreshment stand. There were sandcastles with moats all over the place that day. Billy went down, hands clutching at falling crockery, adding another layer of sand to his wet clothes. He got up and brushed as much sand as he could from his wet clothes and, ignoring the threats from the sandcastle builder, collected the crockery: cups, jug, teapot and its disconnected spout.

'Can I 'ave me deposit back please?' Billy reached up and one by one carefully placed the crockery on the counter of the stand, the spout last.

'You've broken the teapot! Bloody-'ell, that's the third one today, that is!' The man behind the counter placed the cups on the shelf behind him, ready for the next customer.

'Can I 'ave me six-pence deposit back, please?' Billy repeated, patiently.

'I told you, didn' I? You broke me teapot, so you can't 'ave it back. Now sod off!'

Billy was horrified. 'But you'll 'ave to gimme me deposit, me mam'll batter me if I don't gerrit back.'

'An' I'll batter you if you don't sod off! Now sod off!'

Billy was in a no-win situation: stay put and demand his deposit, and he would be battered by the owner of the teapot; go back to his mam and he would be battered by the owner of the deposit. He turned and stared out across the river to the distant silhouette of The Liver Buildings, wondering if his twenty-five yard swimming certificate guaranteed a safe escape back home.

He wended his way back to the seawall, ploughing his way through castles. 'The man wouldn't gimme me deposit back, Mam.' Billy stood over his mother. She looked up at her sodden, sand covered offspring, nodded silently, and returned to her study of the distant horizon.

'Can we go to the fair, now, Mam?' Terry pleaded.

'I suppose so, now I've promised,' she replied. 'Are you all right?' she hovered over Billy's mother. 'We'll just take them there and then we can go home.'

Billy's mother glanced towards the heavens. Would this day never end?

We walked back up the slip way to the promenade. Thousands of day-trippers were taking advantage of the hot sunny day: strolling along the prom, laughing, shouting or rendered mute by mouthfuls of ice cream and candy-floss.

Terry hovered around a Wall's 'Stop me and Buy one' cart. 'Can we 'ave a cornet Mam?' He clutched the rail on the cart. ''Ow much is a cornet, mister?' He ignored the large sign advertising 'Cornets 3d.'

The ice cream man pointed to the sign. 'Thri'pence each, with free raspberry syrup, son; but only if you buy 'em right now.'

'Ey, Mam, quick! Gerrem now, the raspberry's free!'

'Do you want one?' Terry's mother asked her still silent friend. She shook her head.

'Five cornets, please; with raspberry.'

The five cornets were demolished before we reached the entrance to the fairground.

'What's 'appening there?' Georgie pointed to a tall red-and-white striped canvas tent-like structure with a tiny stage on top, surrounded by hordes of small children sitting on the ground.

'Oooh, it's ages since I've seen one of them.' Terry's mother walked over and stood behind the back row of children.

'Warrisit?' Georgie stood alongside her.

'It's a Punch and Judy show, you'll like it. Here we are, you lot sit down and watch the show.'

We all sat down behind the audience, then Billy shuffled forward, pushing little girls and boys out of his way, until he reached the front row. After a few minutes expectant silence, the curtains across the tiny stage slid back, to reveal Mr Punch sitting with his legs dangling over the edge of the stage. 'Good afternoon ladies and gentlemen, girls and boys.' Half the audience squealed with delight and the other half screamed in terror at the unearthly high-pitched voice emanating from the distorted puppet.

A string of sausages suddenly appeared over the edge of the stage, pulled by Mr Punch. This was too much for some of the more impressionable amongst the audience. They scrambled to their feet and fled into the arms of their mothers.

Billy studied Mr Punch and the sausages. 'They're not real, there's someone in there speakin',' he swivelled round to address the remaining audience. 'You don' 'ave to be frightened, 'e's not real.'

Mr Punch pointed the sausages at Billy and addressed him in a squeaky whisper. 'Sod off, you. Go on, bugger-off.'

Billy was a bit taken aback. 'I only meant there was no need for 'em to

128

be frightened,' Billy protested. 'I only meant there was someone in the tent speakin' an' not you.'

'Well it is me, and if you don't sod off, I'll come down there an' knock your bloody head off.' Mr Punch shook the sausages at Billy. The unearthly squeak adopted a distinctly menacing tone. There was something very unnerving about a wooden puppet, its paint peeling, threatening violence with a string of sausages. Billy shuffled backwards, out of range.

The Punch and Judy show got under way with increasing action from an assortment of dogs and crocodiles, with Mrs Punch taking the brunt of her husband's penchant for domestic violence.

This was just up Billy's street. He cheered each blow wildly, shouting encouragement when the action tailed off a bit. His mother watched his antics with growing alarm, as did the children sitting close to him. They edged away, fearful that his enthusiasm might end up with him joining the mayhem with them as the victims.

'Billy! Billy! Come here, luv,' Terry's mother saw the haggard look of despair on her friend's face. 'Come on, we're going to the fair now.'

Billy was torn between the show and the fair, but the fair won as Punch announced the end of the show and advised that shortly a hat would be passed around the parents in order for them to express their appreciation for the performance.

Reference to the hat added urgency to Terry's mother's request. 'Come back here now, Billy, or I'll batter your bloody head off.'

Billy stood up. 'Told you it wasn't real, didn' I? Look there 'e is, 'e's the one that's been shovin' Mr Punch around an' makin 'im speak.'

The showman appeared from behind the tent with Punch hanging by the leg from his hand. 'I've told you, haven't I? I'll knock your sodden 'ead off!' The showman held Mr Punch aloft and shook him at Billy. He'd forgotten to take his squeaker out of his mouth, and the sight of Mr Punch being swung by the legs by a man with a high-pitched squeak, threatening violence, again unnerved Billy.

He ran like hell for his mother.

Across the promenade, opposite the pier, the fairground was in full swing. Proprietors of sideshows bawled out the excitements of their shows. 'It's all 'ere! Cum an' see the ninth wunder of the world! She's hairy, she's big: bigger than an effelant. Come along an' see the bearded lady, if you dare! Only tuppence, ladies an' gennelmen!'

'Rollup! Rollup! Three goes for a thri'penny joey!' A bowler hatted stallholder set his coconuts in carefully moulded immovable mounts.

Gaudily painted horses bobbed up and down on twisted gilded poles, whirling round in a race with no end. Waltzers hurtled around their tracks, rising and falling, cars revolving at great speed on their pivots as scruffy youths obliged the riders by heaving them into a spin. The fair was a deafening, in both sound and colour, melee of pure excitement.

'Can we 'ave a go on that, an' on that, an' on tharraswell?' Terry pointed in all directions.

'Right, now you lot, we've only got enough money for two goes each, so you pick which ones you want, but you're not goin' on the Waltzer and you not goin' on that either.' Terry's mother indicated the bucket seats, suspended by chains, full of squealing passengers, whirling high above our heads.

There was no point in wasting time arguing. In any case she hadn't excluded the most exciting of them all: the Caterpillar. Billy led the rush to the green canvas tube that had just come to a halt on its undulating track.

'And you can't go on that either!' she shouted. But it was too late; we dived under the convoluted hood, into the darkness and sat together in the front carriage.

'That'll be one-an'-thri'pence.' Terry's mother handed over the fare. She knew there was no way of extricating us from the belly of the caterpillar.

The openings in the canvas hood crawled over to shut us into complete darkness. I could feel Tommy stiffen in his seat. There was a hiss of steam, then the carriage began to roll. Slowly, slowly, faster, faster, the carriage accelerated, rising and falling, faster and faster, louder and louder.

My hands hurt as they gripped the handrail in front of me. I was absolutely terrified, but it was Georgie who was the first to give vent to his feelings. 'I want me mam!' he screamed in terror as the carriage lurched and swayed in its mad career around the track. 'I wanner gerroff! I want me mam!'

'Bloody great, this is!' Billy stood up, though he still gripped the rail. 'Bloody smashin', this!'

I was just about to join Georgie in his plea for salvation, when the Caterpillar began to slow down, then rumble to a halt. Blessed daylight flooded the carriages as the hood folded back.

Georgie, Terry, Tommy and me staggered unsteadily to our feet and swayed our way back to our minders. Billy remained in the carriage. 'I'm 'avin another go, that was smashin', that was. I'll 'ave me other go on this, Mam.' His mother was still staring into space.

'You wasn't supposed to go on that in the first place, now come here!' It was left to Terry's mother to recover Billy.

'Why don't you all go on that one, that's nice that one is.' She walked us to a roundabout of swings about half the diameter of the one we'd seen before, and rotating at about a tenth of the speed at ground level.

'That's for kids, tharris! I don' wanner go on that sissy thing!' Billy dismissed the idea.

'Well what about that one?' She pointed to a red train with open carriages, sedately puffing round a flat track.

We ignored her.

'I think I'll go an 'ave a look in there, instead of goin' on another ride.' Billy strolled over to a sideshow with a huge banner advertising 'Straight from Ripley's *Believe It or Not!*', and underneath, a description of the delights to be found behind the curtain: 'See the dog with no head, Wonder at the five-legged sheep, Marvel at the two-headed snake, and the goat with two heads. Freaks of nature from all over the world. They are all here if you dare to look!'

'What d'you think Queenie, there's no harm in it, I suppose?' Terry's mother looked doubtfully at her friend.

Billy's mother nodded. Dark thoughts entered her mind: maybe they'd keep Billy and give him a job as a minder of the exhibits, or more likely, a job as an exhibit.

'Five children, please.' She handed over another one and thri'pence. Billy led the way through the curtain. We were the only visitors.

A low circular wooden barrier decorated with gory pictures of animals with an assortment of additional legs and organs and hairy human beings with a few useful extra appendages, barred our way. Inside the ring, the ground was covered by a thick layer of sawdust. The 'freaks' sat around the edge of the ring, chewing their way through small mounds of rotting vege-tables. A scrawny sheep with something tied to one of its front legs, had a notice draped over its back announcing that it was a 'Five-legged sheep. The only known example of its kind.'

A billy goat glanced up as we entered, then returned to munching his vegetables with one of its heads, pushing a bunch of hair with horns stuck in it, hanging from a short length of string, out of his way.

We wandered round the outside of the ring.

'Where's the snake wiv two 'eads? An' where's the dog? I can't see no dog, an' there's no humin beins?' Georgie leaned over the barrier to make sure he had not missed anything.

Billy leaned over, trying to get a hold of the billy goat, but it shuffled out of his reach. 'I wanner proper look at 'im, you can't see 'is other 'ead prop'ly from 'ere.' He was anxious to get a detailed examination of nature's mistakes, so that he could add to his already extensive knowledge of suffering.

''Ere they are, 'ere.' Tommy was in a corner of the tent, studying a row of big glass jars set on a shelf. 'Aww, look at this.'

The jars contained a variety of off-white lumps, suspended in cloudy yellow liquid. 'Here's the dog wiv no 'ead!' Tommy reached up and poked a jar labelled 'Headless Dog from America'. Something vaguely resembling a hairless animal oscillated in the liquid.

'Look, it 'asn't gorran 'ead!' Billy poked the jar again.

We peered at the swaying object. I couldn't see any tail either, in fact I couldn't see anything that remotely resembled a dog.

'An' here's a snake!' Terry shook another jar. Two snakes rolled around in the cloudy liquid, tied together by their tails.

'This must be a two-'eaded snake.' Billy studied the exhibit. 'Look, it says on the jar, irris the two-'eaded snake!'

Georgie examined the jar in great detail. 'Bloody swiz, this is. That's norrer two-'eaded snake, it just two snakes tied together, bloody swiz. It's bloody robbery in 'ere!'

Billy took down the headless dog. 'Christ, this is a bloody swiz an' all. This is norrer dog, I don't know warritis!' He made his way along the shelf, shaking the bottles, muttering 'robbery' as the shapeless freaks circulated their jars.

'Worrer you fink you're-a doin'!'

We froze in our tracks. An enormous hulk of a man stood in the entrance. He was bare from the waist up except for a coloured handkerchief tied round his neck and a montage of tattoos all over his arms and torso. We gaped at his awesome presence.

Petrified with fright, Billy dropped the headless dog. It hit the ground and the yellow liquid began to ooze out of the jar, creeping through the sawdust. Billy was transfixed by the sight of the escaping fluid, horrified by the magnitude of what he had done. The rest of us had no such problem. We dived under the tent between the guy ropes, and fled back to the safety of our chaperones.

'Where's Billy?' Terry's mother saw the look of fear in our faces. 'What has he done now?'

Before we could answer, the curtain parted and Billy appeared, held by the scruff of the neck by the tattooed giant. His mother looked at the pair of them with something like relief in her eyes. It seemed that perhaps Billy was to be taken for a job with the freak show. She was sure he had found his niche in life.

'If I knew who you were wiv, they'd pay for the damage you did before I let you go, they would.' The tattooed man let go of Billy's neck and propelled him on his way with a kick to his backside.

Billy ran towards us. His mother turned her back and hurried into the crowd with the rest of us closely following. It was bad enough getting Billy back, she certainly didn't want to have to pay for him.

'That was a swiz, that was, Mam.' Terry tugged at his mother's coat. 'It wasn't worth it, it was robbery. Can we 'ave a go on something worth the money?'

'Sorry, luv, but we're nearly skint now,' she replied.

'Aar-ey, Mam, just one more go,' Terry pleaded.

'What do you think, Queenie, just one more go, then we can all go home?' She took Billy's mother's hand. The magic of the word 'home' brought life back to Billy's mother's face. One more ride and she could sail the River Mersey towards the end of this awful day. She cheered up. 'Ok, then, one more go, then we go home.'

'You can go on that one.' Our minders headed over to the red train.

Before we could argue, Billy's mother delved in her purse for the last of her money. 'Five children, please.' She handed her one and thri'pence to a young girl at the entrance to the track.

We trooped through and mounted the carriage steps. It was hardly the most dangerous ride, but it was better than nothing. In any case, memories of the Caterpillar were still fresh in our minds.

''Ere y'are, missus, you've give me too much.' The young girl handed back a thri'penny joey. 'It's only thri'pence each and there's only four of them.'

'No, luv, there's five.' Billy's mother counted us. Georgie, Terry, Tommy, me! The young girl was right, Billy was missing!

'Oh, no!' the haunted look of despair returned to her face.

'Where the hell's he gone to now?' Terry's mother scanned the crowds.

NEW BRIGHTON FAIRGROUND

Across the promenade, opposite the Pier, the fairground was in full swing

133

Billy's mother said nothing. She just wanted to go home, with or without Billy.

''E must 'ave got lost when we ran away from that man,' said Georgie, helpfully.

'Coo-ee Billy!' Terry's mother yelled, 'coo-ee, we're here!' Several in the milling crowds turned round at the piecing summons, but there was still no sign of Billy.

'Shall we go an' 'ave a look for him, Mam?' Terry suggested. 'If you gimme thri'pence I can go up there an' look out for 'im.' He pointed up at the whirling swings high over head.

'No, nobody move! Christ, we'll end up looking for all of you. Now stay right close to us or I'll marmalise the lot of you!' She was adamant.

We trooped round the fairground for about half an hour, searching the crowds; all except Billy's mother. She kept her eyes firmly on the ground. There was no sign of him, and it was beginning to get late.

Suddenly, Georgie spotted a policeman. 'He'll help us find him, Mam.'

His mother ran over to the bobby. 'Excuse me constable, but we've lost a little boy.'

The policeman tilted his helmet back and looked at her without answering for a good few seconds. And then, 'His name's not Billy, by chance, is it?'

Terry's mother hesitated. How come the policeman knew his name? What had he done now? Had justice finally caught up with him and locked him up? 'It might be,' she compromised.

'You must know the name of your own son, missus, now is his name Billy, or what?'

'Yes, it's Billy all right, but it's her son, not mine,' she pointed to her friend.

The policeman crooked his finger as an instruction for us to follow him. He led the way to the fairground entrance then a little way along the prom-enade to a wooden hut with a sign on the door, 'Lost Children'.

'Is that him?' The bobby opened the door to reveal Billy sitting forlornly on a stool in the corner of the hut. She nodded. 'Now then, madam, I think you'll have to do something about him,' the bobby said, sternly.

Billy's mother needed no telling. She'd already given a lot of thought to what she was going to do with Billy, now that he had been turned down by the freak show.

It seems that Billy, having found himself alone, had made his way back to the freak show, just in case we had gone back, only to see the tattooed man going off somewhere, to be replaced by a boy not much older than Billy. Billy decided he would advise the boy just how much of a swiz the show was, tell him it wasn't his fault that the jar got broken, and then demand his money back plus a free look at the freaks.

The resultant scuffle was in full swing when the tattooed man reappeared. Billy's future was only secured by the chance passing of the policeman.

'He tried to wreck the show, he broke one of their best exhibits, and they are very rare they are, the owner told me. That's malicious damage, that is.' The bobby shook his finger at Billy's mother. 'And he tried to get in without paying: that's fraud, that is,' he continued. 'Then he attacked the owner's son. That's assault, that is.'

Billy's mother stood silently with her head down, listening to the list of crimes, wondering what would happen if she advised the policeman that he was also guilty of throwing dead jellyfish at people, wrecking sandcastles, robbery with violence, and being a foul mouthed bully with little girls. Maybe he'd be arrested on the spot and sent to jail for a month or two. But she reluctantly decided against it. That woman on the tram might appear for him and give evidence of her attempts to abandon Billy by running away from him from the tram, and then refusing to pay his fare for the ferry.

Then she brightened up a little. She could now go home, and what she did with Billy when she got home was her own business, something to look forward to.

'Don't worry, constable, I'll make sure he doesn't do anything wrong again. And I'm very sorry for all the trouble he's caused,' she smiled sweetly at the policeman. 'Just leave it to me, I'll do something about it,' she added, eyes glinting with a determination to definitely do something about it.

The Liverpool ferry strained at its moorings on the pier, anxious to make a start for home.

It was still early evening. Most of the day-trippers were obviously determined to get as much as they could for their fare and had opted for the last ferry home, so it was strangely quiet as we boarded.

We gazed down at the bustling hordes on the beach and along the promenade, across in the fairground and all along the pier. It was wonderful, a magical scene, happy excited crowds spending their pocket money on frivolities instead of necessities for once, or just being happy. A day's escape from routine; a day at the seaside.

The gangplanks were raised, the muddy water boiled and the ferry swung into the wide Mersey. Seagulls hung motionless, carried by the wake of the speeding boat, begging tit-bits with raucous cries, but we sat in silence as the Liver Building shed its haze and grew in size.

Even as we left the ferry and made our way up the floating tunnel and along the Pier Head to the tram stop, we were quiet, each reliving the memory of our day at New Brighton.

Billy's mother seemed particularly engrossed in her own thoughts. She contemplated the day's events and their effects on the future of her family. She had been accused of, at best, attempted embezzlement by trying to defraud Liverpool Corporation of a tram fare and a ferry fare, or, at worst, of trying to abandon her own child, twice. Even worse than that, she had nurtured a criminal, a violent robber, a foul mouthed bully, a destroyer of sandcastles, a wrecker of sideshows, an embezzler; a hooligan.

As she sat down on the tram, she carefully retrieved the five children's penny return tickets from her purse, and turned round to count us. Yes, there were five: Georgie, Tommy, me, Terry and, beaming with pleasure at the memory of an exciting day at the seaside, Billy.

The Westminster Chimes

'We watched him, in awe of the art of the clockmaker: marvelling at his skill and the magical way yet another spring skipped out of the clock and danced along the counter.'

The best laid schemes o' mice an' men
Gang aft a-gley.

Robert Burns

Westminster Chimes Clock

'YOU COMING OUT OR WHAT?'

Terry's shout through the letterbox and insistent banging on our front door summoned me from the kitchen where I was trying to get Tibby, our cat, to sit up and beg.

'For Christ's sake, do it like this!' I hauled Tibby back onto his haunches for the umpteenth time. 'That's it, like that.' As soon as I let go, Tibby made a dash to get under the cooker.

Tibby, I decided, was a bit thick, and I wondered if I could swap him for Charlie Jones' dog, Bruce. Bruce could sit up and beg, and not only that, he would play dead on command. Bruce wasn't thick, but the trouble was that Charlie wasn't thick either. I gave up the idea and went to answer the door.

Terry was leaning on the railings and behind him, sucking at what looked like a piece of old rope, was Georgie, for once without his older brother, Billy. Georgie was all right and a good mate; though he was a bit slow-witted. Billy on the other hand, showed all the early symptoms of a

137

psychopath, never hitting anyone if he could kick them, and never kicking them if he could get hold of something more lethal than a boot. The last time I saw him he was declaring himself 'King of the Castle', having hurled some poor urchin off the roof of an air raid shelter.

Billy was apparently stricken by some childhood complaint on this particular day, and so Georgie was playing out by himself.

Georgie and Billy lived nearly opposite me with their mam, next door to their cousin, Lily. I think their dad lived somewhere else because we never saw him; and neither Billy nor Georgie ever mentioned him.

Despite the absence of a father they were both as well looked after as their mother's income from doing other peoples washing would allow.

Georgie was the only one I knew who had a jumper that actually fitted him and was more or less intact. He wore it today. It was bright red, adding a touch of colour to his otherwise drab outfit: grey short trousers and black socks stuck into dirty white plimsolls.

He was tall for his age and his chubby round face always shone with a healthy glow from under a mop of dark brown hair. His mam cut his hair to save money; and to keep the job simple she cut in a horizontal line right around his head at just above eye level. The result was that Georgie's hair seemed to have nothing permanently to do with Georgie, it looked as though some sort of semi-spherical, hairy animal, had taken refuge on top of his head.

He stood quietly behind Terry, chewing away. His mouth was black and yellowy black juice ran down his chin.

Terry noticed him for the first time. 'Giz a suck.'

Without a word, Georgie pulled the sodden liquorice root from his mouth and handed it to Terry. 'Spud can 'ave a suck as well if 'e wants to,' said Georgie. Something was afoot. Georgie was not given to such extremes of generosity, particularly where 'sticky lice' was concerned. He obviously wanted something.

"Ow about going to Prinny Park?' Terry suggested, between sucks.

Georgie interrupted. 'Said you could 'ave a suck. Didn't say you could eat the bloody lot, did I? Anyway,' he grabbed the remains of his liquorice stick and turned to me, 'our Billy says you owe 'im tuppence an' he wants it back, now.' He emphasised the 'now'.

Even from his sick bed, Billy exerted influence.

It was true, I did owe him tuppence; but the chance of paying the whole lot back was remote, at least for the next week or so. 'I'll give 'im a penny now and the rest next week,' I offered.

'Ok, that'll do. He said you can give it to me an' 'e said I could spend it at Ma Mottram's.'

Reluctantly I passed over the penny, a brand-new shiny one that I had jealously kept for weeks; my entire wealth. I knew that there was no way Billy would give Georgie anything, let alone money; but I reasoned that if I later informed Billy that I had given the whole tuppence to Georgie, it would be Georgie's problem to prove otherwise.

Georgie grabbed the penny and dashed off slapping his backside with one hand and urging his imaginary horse to greater efforts. 'Gee-up, Trigger. I bags being Hopalong Cassidy!'

Terry set off after him similarly encouraging his mount, claiming his right to being Gene Autry, and firing a Colt 45 shaped hand at Georgie.

I couldn't think of another cowboy's name; so ignoring history and geography, I declared myself Robin Hood, and followed.

We ran along the jigger that cut the street in half, zig-zagging across the next street and colliding to a halt in front of Mottram's shop in Ashbridge Street. We squashed our faces to the grimy window.

Ma Mottram could just be made out in the gloom, standing behind the tiny wooden counter, surrounded on all sides by bulging shelves of everything imaginable. She was a short stout woman with no teeth, yellow skin and a moustache.

There were boxes of Oxos perched on jars of sweets, and jars of sweets balanced on cartons of Persil. Garlands of clothes-pegs and cards of buttons vied for position with skipping ropes and reels of ribbons. The floor was piled with bundles of firewood, mops and brushes, and small bags of coal that worked out at five times the price of a sack from the coalman – but then who could afford a sackful? A bacon slicer stood at one end of the counter alongside a fly-specked slab of cheese and a great pat of butter that some said had been there as long as Ma Mottram – twenty years.

Faint gaslight from a broken mantle filtered between the Craven 'A' and Bisto advertisements on the only window, but Ma Mottram didn't seem to need light, she just reached out into the gloom without looking and found whatever her customers wanted, or pointed for them to help themselves. She never moved from the spot and some reckoned she took up her position when her mother dropped dead on the same spot twenty years ago, and had been there ever since.

Georgie burst into the shop. 'Pennuth of peanut butter please!' he blurted it out, gasping for breath.

'Let me 'ave your penny first,' Ma demanded, well versed in the ways of kids. Ma's ever-present cigarette jerked up and down between clenched lips as she spoke, adding fresh flecks of ash to the layer of dust that covered the counter.

Georgie handed over the shiny coin.

She plucked the fag from her mouth and carefully set it on the edge of the butter pat, sending another inch of ash to join the small heaps on the counter. Ma wiped her hands on her pinny, transferring some of its many stains to her fingers. Licking a finger she deftly flicked a small piece of greaseproof paper from a pile on the counter, then using an old spoon kept especially for the purpose, she measured out a small dollop of peanut butter from an open tin.

Georgie waited, hoping for another measure.

'There's your penny-worth, now 'op it; and tell your mam that if she doesn't settle up what she owes me by tomorrow, she won't get anymore tick from me!' Ma Mottram didn't seem to be talking to anyone in particular, she didn't have to. She said it to all her customers because all their names appeared on her slate early in the week, though only on condition that the slate was wiped clean before the weekend, otherwise it was cash only come next Monday.

We trooped outside. Georgie divided up the peanut butter into three little heaps: half for himself and the other half between Gizzo and me.

It had all gone before we reached our street, as Georgie finally abandoned licking the paper in the search for any remains in the cracks of the greaseproof.

'Don't suppose you've got another tuppence 'ave you, Spud?' Georgie asked, hopefully.

I was right! Billy was not a party to our recent transaction. But I could not help admiring Georgie. He must have known that when his older brother got the facts, Georgie would be in trouble – the kind of trouble that was painful. As soon as Billy realised his money had been spent he would go bezerk, and Georgie would suffer: all for the sake of a pennuth of peanut butter, which he'd shared out. Yes, Georgie had to be admired, but from now on he was on his own.

It suddenly dawned on Terry, what Georgie had done; and he too decided it was best not to be linked with the deception. Terry was off at a fast run with no thought of Gene Autry, only an urgent desire to put as much distance between himself and Billy's sick bed. Billy might make a sudden recovery when he got the facts. I followed Terry.

Georgie hesitated, then decided to get it over with sooner than later. He walked back along the jigger towards home, his hands stuffed resolutely into his pockets. It would not be the first time he had suffered pain at his brother's hands. Maybe, in Georgie's rather plodding way of thinking, he reasoned that at least he deserved it this time.

He quickened his pace, absorbed in trying to walk as fast as he could without treading on the joints between the uneven paving slabs.

I eventually caught up with Terry at his house. Terry's family lived just

AIR RAID SHELTER

...he was declaring himself 'King of the Castle', having hurled some poor urchin off the roof of an air raid shelter

down the street on the same side as us, but ten houses away. He lived with his mother and his older brother by four years, Alan.

A father didn't exist. My mother said he had died before the family moved to our street. Two other brothers, twins and a bit older than Terry, appeared from time to time then disappeared to some place called 'a home'.

Alan wouldn't tell us what a home was and Terry didn't know. When we asked the twins during one of their infrequent visits to see their mother, they didn't seem to know either, muttering vaguely about someone called an ''ouse mam' in a 'bloody big 'ouse'.

Terry's mother, Maggie to the adults, was 'a right one' according to our various mothers; though, we never got to know exactly what a 'right one' was, except that it had something to do with Maggie having lost her husband five years ago, and not staying in permanent mourning.

It appears that she took advantage of no longer being enslaved by marriage by going out and staying in with a steady stream of substitute husbands, insisting that Terry and Alan call them all uncles. Apparently, one or two real husbands in our street had tried to become one of her substitute ones, and that had upset their wives for some reason or other.

Terry couldn't understand what all the fuss was about at the time. He

141

didn't mind calling anyone an uncle, particularly as they were a source of extra pocket money.

Terry's mam took it all philosophically. She didn't want any substitutes from our street anyway: there were plenty of other streets and some of them had American servicemen living in them. Americans, unlike the locals, could add regularly to her food ration, as well as providing the odd pair of ladies' stockings.

Once the local dads had given up, their wives soon forgot and Terry's mother joined them in their endless gossiping, expeditions to the shops, and occasional visits to The Brick. Terry's mother did like a drop of pale-ale and if pale-ale was in short supply, any other shade seemed to be just as acceptable.

Whilst it took some time for her to be accepted in the street, Terry became my best mate and one of the gang the minute he came out to play.

Terry was about the same height as me and stocky, but with a mop of brown hair tinged with red. His face was liberally sprinkled with freckles, which gradually congealed to form his small blotchy-brown turned-up nose.

Just like me, he was clad in his brother's hand-me-downs: short, grey trousers with shiny bums, which, if anything, were baggier around the legs than mine, and a blue shirt with buttons salvaged from a variety of garments. The shirt and most of his trousers were hidden by an enormous much darned jumper.

From the day we met, Terry and I were the best and closest of friends, sharing all our worldly possessions and thoughts, including some we shouldn't have had at our age.

We loved exactly the same things: from Sevvy Park to the Pier Head and hurling stones at our many rivals from the streets around Lodge Lane.

Terry's older brother, Alan, was accepted as a valuable addition to the street's inhabitants the moment his enormous ears made their first appearance. Alan was mad: not the really violent kind of mad, except when his ears were brought to his attention, but the kind of mad more usually described as crackers: 'Touched!' Nin would say, or 'Sixpence short of a shilling.'

Alan's looks fitted his reputation. He was tall and thin with trousers at half-mast, lank hair always in his eyes and a permanent vacant grin. Not only that, but his head seemed too long and too thin for his height and it appeared to be kept upright by the sail-like effect of his enormous ears, sticking out at right angles. In frontal silhouette, he looked vaguely similar to a wing nut on a pole.

He was given to bursting out in hysterical laughter for no apparent reason. Alan was definitely 'touched'.

With the peanut butter only a lingering taste, Terry and I sat down on his step. 'Our clock's bust,' he announced, breaking the silence. 'And Uncle John was late for work.'

The latest uncle had apparently dashed out of the house that morning without even saying goodbye to Terry.

'Me mam told me to take it to Eggertons to gerrit fixed, but I forgot.'

The clock he referred to was a particularly good example of the Westminster Chime variety to be found on many a mantelpiece around Lodge Lane. It was the most valuable thing in the house.

'What's up wiv it?' I asked, interested in the idea of going to Eggertons, a tiny clock-repairer's shop next to the Post Office. You couldn't see what was inside the shop because the window was full of fascinating bits of clocks and watches and a large cardboard sign proclaiming 'Watch and Clock Experts. Time-pieces repaired by Craftsmen', together with a more optimistic notice saying 'Gold and Silver bought and sold and anything else valuable. Best prices paid.'

'The chime's gone; but I think the fingers are all right,' replied Terry, not absolutely sure about the fingers because he was still learning to tell the time.

'Why don't you go and gerrit so we can 'ave a look in Eggertons?' I suggested.

Ten minutes later we were standing outside the shop with Terry clutching the broken clock. After a few minutes to pluck up courage, we went in. The door tripped a tiny bell. Before it stopped ringing, Mr Eggerton appeared out of the depths of the workshop somewhere at the back of the shop.

He turned out to be a small spherical man with a round face and thick spectacles with semi-spherical lenses, a completely bald round head and a bulging stomach so round that his hands could hardly reach the counter. Terry instantly christened him Humpty Dumpty, but kept it to himself until later.

The shop was all we thought it might be. Clock cases big and small, some grotesquely ornate and others elegantly simple, were heaped all over the floor and occupied every inch of the massive shelves along the back wall. One particularly gaudy black and brass carriage clock stood at the end of the counter with a notice propped against it stating: 'Not for sale.' The clock stood as a showpiece of Mr Eggerton's craftsmanship. It was about twenty-five minutes fast.

'What do you want?' he glared at us with big round watery eyes magnified by the semi-spherical lenses in his glasses.

'Me mam said could you fix this?' Terry lifted the clock onto the counter with some difficulty. We were just able to peer over the counter on tiptoe.

The clockmaker dragged Terry's clock to the middle of the counter and proceeded to wind it up. It tick-tocked steadily as the clockmaker put his ear to the case.

'Chime's gone,' Terry volunteered.

Humpty Dumpty's magnified eyes peered at us across the counter as he informed us that further advice was unnecessary, or words to that effect.

We kept quiet as the master craftsman began his work. He set about the clock with an array of delicate instruments and a large screwdriver, pausing from time to time to scrutinise the works with the aid of an eyeglass.

Ten minutes later the clock was in bits and the counter strewn with springs and cogs and levers of all shapes and sizes.

We watched him, in awe of the art of the clockmaker: marvelling at his skill and the magical way yet another spring skipped out from the clock and danced along the counter. He was a genius. How anyone could understand such wonderful intricacy, we just did not know.

He again studied each of the myriad pieces carefully with his eyeglasses screwed into one eye, and then suddenly produced a large brown paper bag from under the counter. With exaggerated care he scooped most of the parts into a heap and swept them over the edge of the counter into the bag.

'Nothing I can do about that,' he stated, and disappeared into the back.

We stared at the bag on the counter.

It took some time for the reality to sink in; and when it did, the sheer horror of the situation gradually dawned on Terry. He had left the house with a more or less intact and fine example of a Westminster Chimes Clock, keeping good time and having only the inconvenience of a silent chime. He would return home with a brown paper bag, full of bits.

Terry was in a no win situation. Whatever he said, it was going to be his fault. Pale faced and in silence we set off back home.

There was only one hope of salvation: a new uncle might appear. Apart from being a pretty good source of pocket money, they always seemed intent on getting on his side and making friends with him for some reason or other.

The thought of a new uncle, or even the return of an old one cheered him up a bit and he quickened his pace, still clutching the brown paper bag.

We weaved our way against the tide of women carrying shopping bags. Many trailed their infants, their child's arms outstretched, almost airborne as their little legs skipped sideways at ten to the dozen, dragged along by mothers in a hurry to finish their shopping.

Terry was using the brown paper bag as a kind of path clearer. I suppose he thought everyone would realise it contained his mam's precious clock and would automatically get out of his way.

Most did, but one did not.

'Gerrout of the way!' A big lady with a blotchy red face, ham arms, and legs like tree trunks, engulfed Terry as he collided with her.

She was made up of great globs of flesh, and her voluminous polka dotted dress was not so much worn as stuffed full of her. She was moving like a galleon in full sail and barely faltered in her stride, as Terry bounced off her, sending him sprawling in the gutter.

The brown paper bag burst open.

It was very interesting to watch: little brass cogs careered off at speed, racing each other along the gutter, some steering a straight course for yards with others veering off in graceful curves into the path of a milk cart. Several disappeared down a grid. Little springs hopped hastily after them.

Terry sat in the gutter, thoughtfully considering the situation, rubbing the knee that had broken his fall with one hand, and wiping his nose with his other. Then he picked up the clock case which had survived almost intact and methodically gathered up all he could find of the works, carefully placing them in the case.

'That'll be enough,' he declared, prising a flattened spring out of a crack in the gutter. 'I expect I can purrit together and gerrit working. Most of the stuff down the grid is probably to do with the chimes and they weren't workin' anyway.'

Ever since watching the master clockmaker's final efforts, I had been giving serious thought to the consequences of accompanying Terry all the way home. I had seen his mother venting her wrath on Terry before, and she had a habit of including anyone with him in the proceedings.

The sight of the cogs tinkling down the grid decided it. I was off

Later that day I found Terry sitting on his doorstep surrounded by the pips and stalks of half a dozen apples. Everything else had been eaten. He grinned at me. 'I'd 'ave saved you a bit if you'd been 'ere,' Terry greeted me.

It seems a new uncle had duly arrived.

Throwing a protective arm around Terry he promised to get another clock, and then offered him a thri-penny bit and some apples if he promised to play out for the day.

I wanted to know how come Terry had so many kind-hearted uncles, and I didn't. I set off home to ask my mother.

The Collectors

'We were baffled. We all knew the temptations of Woolworth's shelves, piled high with sweets and toys; but Terry had stolen a bar of soap!'

My object all sublime
I shall achieve in time
To let the punishment fit the crime.

Patience, W. S. Gilbert

SOLWAY ARMS

(Corner of Alt and Solway Street) (Grandad) ... had been barred out of most pubs in the area from time to time, but the bar seldom lasted for more than a day or two. The drop in sales of Mild Ale soon assured his return

'I'LL SWAP YOU THIS ONE FOR YOUR CAPSTAN FULL STRENGTH.'
Terry held out a piece of dirty, crumpled cardboard.

'Worrisit?' I demanded.

'It's a rare one, it's American. Gorrit from a Yank me mam knows; me Uncle ... err ... me Uncle worrever is name is.'

Normally, claiming to get something from an American would have raised some scepticism; but Terry's mother seemed to get a lot of visits from American soldiers, sometimes two at a time, introducing them to Terry as his uncles, then sending him out to play.

'So bloody mucky, I can't see worritis. Worrisit?' I asked again.

'Lucky Strike!' Terry replied, proudly. 'That's worritis, if you wanna know: a Lucky bloody Strike. An' just because it's a bit dirty doesn't mean it's not valuable. Anyway are you gunner swap your Capstan for it, or not?'

We sat with our backs against the toilet wall in the backyard of No. 43, surrounded by our collections of cigarette packets. Yesterday's rummaging in the litter bins on Lodge Lane had yielded an empty ten-packet of Capstan Full Strength. I already had one, but Terry didn't.

'I'll give you a Wills No. 3 for it.' Georgie entered the bargaining. 'I don't mind if it's a bit dirty.'

I was in danger of being gazumped and losing the opportunity of adding a rare foreign specimen to my collection. Grabbing the grubby scrap of cardboard out of Terry's hand, I somewhat reluctantly passed over the brand new Capstan Full Strength packet.

We carefully adjusted our collections into rows and studied each display for possible swaps.

''Ow about givin' me one-a your Park Drive, you've got two?' Georgie leaned over to pick out the duplicate from Terry's collection.

'Buggeroff!' Terry retorted. 'They're not the same: one of 'em's a five an' the other's a ten-packet, an' anyway a ten-packet's worth two five's, so sod off an' get your own.'

Much haggling and some swapping ensued, but after we had finished nobody was satisfied. Someone had something they didn't have.

'I votes we go to town an' find some more,' suggested Billy. 'There's plenty down there, of all different kinds. There's only bloody Woodies round here.' Billy referred to Liverpool's favourite smoke: 'Woodbines', the cheapest ciggy on the market, and sold in ones and twos in most of the shops around Lodge Lane.

'Well I'm goin' to town; who's coming wiv me?' Billy stood up.

Everyone agreed, except Tommy, who had left his little brother Montgomery, playing with some Woody packets outside the back door, in the jigger.

'I can't go,' he said apologetically. 'I've gorra mind Montgomery.'

'Well 'ard bloody luck then,' said Billy, emphatically, "cause we're not 'avin' bloody Gimme Gimme wiv us. Anyway, where is 'e?'

"E's playin' outside in the jigger,' Tommy answered, never lifting his eyes from the tiles, "e's playin' wiv some ciggy packets.'

'Well 'e's a bit quiet isn' 'e; 'e must be eatin' the bloody things. It's the only thing as keeps the greedy sod quiet. 'E's only quiet when 'is gob's full.' Billy's face contorted as he tried to mimic Gimme Gimme's favourite activity: franticly masticating bulging mouth-fulls of anything remotely resembling food.

Tommy got up and unlatched the back door. Sure enough, Montgomery was steadily chewing on a cigarette packet. At least he was quiet and had plenty left to eat, so Tommy closed the door and returned to his seat.

Billy looked at the dejected Tommy, who was again carefully studying the tiles. 'Oh, all bloody right then!' Billy relented, 'you can come; but just walk behind a bit, and keep Gimme Gimme out of the bloody way. Just keep shoving things in 'is gob to keep 'im quiet.'

Tommy's pale face brightened with gratitude. 'Aw, gee thanks Billy, 'e won't be any trouble honest. I'll make sure I walk behind an' keep 'im out of the way. 'E's got plenty to eat, an' they're only Woody packets so it doesn't matter if 'e eats all of 'em.'

Liverpool City's shopping centre, with its litter bins stuffed full of cigarette packets, was about an hour's walk away, and there was always the chance of picking some up on the way; so we debated the best route.

'Along Alt Street, down Parliament Street, by the 'ospital: that's what I reckon.' Terry suggested. 'We might gerra few goin' that way, but it's quicker, and most of 'em will be in the bins in Church Street anyway.'

I ran up the yard and poked my head through the kitchen door. 'Mam, we're goin' to town to collect ciggy packets; an' we've left some in the yard, so don't lerranyone pinch 'em. Mine's gorra Lucky Strike, an' it's rare!'

Her instruction to 'stay in and play, or else!' was lost to us, as we neared the end of the jigger. The narrow alley between the backyards of our street and Ritson Street led to the side of a spacious yard and outbuildings where a haulage business with cart horses once traded. But now it was a bombed site, having received the attention of a Nazi land mine a few years ago.

We dodged around the piles of rubble, all that remained of the buildings, then ran across an expanse of brick-strewn debris on the far side of Alt Street: once the site of a row of terraced houses.

'Loads of dead bodies down there you know,' Billy informed us, as the piles of bricks slowed us down to a walking pace. Billy's conversations always seemed to revert to the subject of pain, or death and destruction, whatever subject he started with. "Undreds of mangled dead bodies,' he continued, warming to the subject. 'All twisted and mangled and burnt; an' dead horses as well.'

We slowed to an untidy halt.

'Whereabouts?' demanded Terry, looking nervously behind him. I don't see none.'

'Under all the bricks, an' down in the cellars,' insisted Billy. 'Down under there.' He pointed to the end wall of a house. The single wall loomed over a mound of rubble, still with the remains of its wallpaper, a grotesque gravestone for the remains of a home.

'All mangled and covered in blood, wiv their guts 'anging out.' Billy savoured his description. 'Stands to reason, they wouldn't bother to pull 'em out of the cellars when the bomb gorrem. What's the point of diggin' 'em out and burying 'em somewhere else. There's no bloody point, they may as well leave 'em where they are.'

I had a vague notion that leaving dead bodies around wasn't allowed, but Billy's reasoning was certainly logical: what was the point of going to all that trouble with a few dead bodies, digging them out and having to bury them again?

Terry had wandered over to the lone wall. 'Looks as though you can get down 'ere to the cellar.' He was pointing to a jumble of plaster and wooden lathes, covering what appeared to be a stairway.

'We'll 'ave a look tomorrow,' I suggested. 'If we go finding dead bodies now, we'll never get to town an' I wanna try and find a Craven "A". Just forget 'em, they'll still be 'ere tomorrow.'

Standing on the rubble under the still decorated wall made me feel strangely uneasy.

I could see the remains of a fireplace, blackened with the soot of its last fire. A window frame poked through the pile of bricks, a tattered rag of a curtain clinging to the charred wood: reminders that this heap of rubble and bricks, was once the home of someone like us.

Gossip amongst the adults in hushed tones had made us vaguely aware that these broken houses were the homes of children and their families, when tragedy struck. But such tragedy was beyond our imagination. The destruction of homes meant nothing more to us than that we had somewhere exciting to play.

Neither could we relate the distant memory of wailing sirens and our scurry to the safety of the air-raid shelters in the darkness of the war years, to the hushed gossip of our mothers telling of others who had not gone to the shelter that night.

'What do we do when we find some?' Terry persisted.

'Drag 'em to the Police Station, bit by bit,' Tommy replied.

I left my uneasy feeling behind as I scrambled down off the remains of the house. The idea of finding dead bodies was quite exiting, though I would prefer to have them all in one piece, but I had serious doubts about taking them to the Police Station. Policeman had a habit of misconstruing our intentions.

A few weeks ago Georgie had explained to a policeman that the reason for pinching apples from the Cash and Carry was to give them to the poor. 'We was playing Robin Hood, and Robin Hood stole from the rich, an' I was gunner give them to the poor, except this one which was goin' a bit bad...'

I had shared his summary punishment. He told the policeman that I was Little John, and that I'd eaten all mine, instead of sticking to his lofty ideals.

After further debate, we decided the deceased could wait until tomorrow. We sauntered off, along Alt Street.

Alt was a long street with rows of terraced houses interrupted by a few corner shops; but dominated by the Roman Catholic Church of St Bernard's and three Walker's Warrington Ale Pubs.

St Bernard's limited its offer of succour to believers of the Catholic faith, whilst the three Walker's Pubs offered sanctuary to anyone with the price for a pint, whatever their faith: a liberal approach much appreciated by the believers before and after a visit to St Bernard's.

We reached the Solway Arms, the biggest of the pubs and the one where Grandad had an occasional pint. 'I sometimes 'ave a couple of 'alves, just to be sociable wiv me mates,' Grandad would say.

'Been sociable again, 'ave we? Christ, if you'd been any more sociable you'd 'ave 'ad to be carried 'ome by your mates.' Grandma Nin opened the door to find him propped against the window ledge, staring fixedly at the doorway, with a leering grin on his face. A half-empty bottle of nut-brown ale sticking out of his jacket pocket bore testament to his socialising until the landlord threw him out.

'I'll just go an' see if me Grandad's in there; never know, 'e might 'ave a ciggy packet.' I knew Grandad tended to become quite generous after socialising in the Solway, particularly near closing time.

We stopped outside the pub, a substantial building of red brick with sandstone sills supporting great carved glass windows displaying the brewer's name amongst flourishes of flowers and Prince of Wales' feathers. The way in was barred by a heavy, yellow-brown varnished door, with an ornate knocker and a well-worn brass latch.

Ever the optimist, I reached up to lift the latch and leaned on the door. The door swung open, and I stuck my head inside.

BOMBED SITE (DEBBIE)

A window frame poked through the pile of bricks, a tattered rag of a curtain clinging to the charred wood: reminders that this heap of rubble and bricks, was once the home of someone like us

The stench was overpowering. Stale tobacco smoke mingled with the musty smell of floorboards marinaded for years in gallons of Walker's Warrington Ales. A collection of men, all with floppy caps on their heads, and all with mufflers round their necks, were propped against the bar. One stood by himself, leaning against a cut glass mirror echoing the same theme as the windows. It was Grandad.

Grandad's cap was pushed back on his head and his muffler dangled untied on his collar-less striped shirt. He wore no jacket, and the bottoms of his voluminous woollen trousers were tied round his ankles by lengths of string.

'It's to keep 'em outer the mud, Missus; on me allotment,' he explained to Nin for the umpteenth time, as she entreated him to 'Try an' look decent' for the umpteenth time.

An enormous pair of First World War army boots confirmed it was Grandad. The boots looked about two-foot long, so big that his mates reckoned they were the only things that kept him upright after a social drink in the Solway.

It wasn't often we got a glimpse of the inside of a pub. For some reason adults were paranoid about keeping children out of them; so much so that we believed there must be something very special about them. Grown-ups kept all the good things for themselves.

I surveyed the scene. The men were propped at regular intervals along the heavy dark wooden bar, which was polished to a glass finish and swilling with ale.

Wooden seats followed the contour of the wall, all the way around the darkened smoke-filled room, encircling half a dozen cast iron tables scattered around the floor: there to add a touch of sophistication and to ensure that any lady clients intent on socialising felt at home. They were piled high with empty pint glasses and overflowing ashtrays. Patches of sawdust on the floorboards tried desperately to lower the level of spilt ale. Fly blown globes over the gas lamps, half without mantles, provided the only illumination. I supposed there must be something special about the place; but, for the life of me, I couldn't spot it.

Turning back to Grandad, I waited patiently whilst he regaled his audience with a story that had something to do with an Englishman, an Irishman and a Scotsman; and a lady on Lime Street.

Whatever it was about must have been funny, because his audience roared with laughter, slapping each other on the back. Then as if someone had given a signal they suddenly became silent and buried their heads back into enormous glasses full of frothing beer.

Grandad rocked back and forth on his two-foot long boots, hooting with laughter. Then he spotted me.

"Ey lads, 'ere's our Kenny! Cummin Kenny, worra you 'avin'? It's my round!' He roared with laughter.

'If 'e comes in, you go out!' The landlord's strident voice cut through the laughter, a voice trained by years of clearing out his customers, just as they started to enjoy themselves.

Grandad was not to be moved. 'It's alright boss, our Kenny's alright; 'e won't cause any problem; unless o' course 'e 'as too many!' Again there were roars of laughter.

'I've warned you,' the landlord reminded Grandad. 'If you don't gerrim out, you're out!'

'I 'opes you're not gunner start fightin' when you've 'ad a few, Kenny,' Grandad beckoned me in.

'Right. That's it! You're barred out for good! The landlord danced up and down with rage as Grandad handed his glass to me, for a swig. 'You're barred bloody out for bloody good! Now finish your ale an' gerrout!'

Grandad retrieved his pint before I could partake, downed it with a single gulp, then with a flamboyant gesture from two fingers, banged the empty glass down on the bar. His mates were arguing furiously with the landlord, trying to get Grandad re-instated; but Grandad didn't seem to care. He had been barred out of most pubs in the area from time to time, but the ban seldom lasted for more than a day or two. The drop in sales of Mild Ale soon assured his return.

He joined us outside the pub. 'Where are you lot off to then?' he inquired.

I wondered whether he was ill or something, because he slurred his words and teetered from toe to heel of his army boots.

'Collectin' ciggy packets, Grandad,' I replied. 'We're going to town ... walking to town 'cause we've got no money for the tram fare. We're goin' so as we can collect ciggy packets, an' we're walkin' cos we've got no money.'

I waited for Grandad's well-known generosity to show itself.

'Cigarette packets, eh ... just a minute.'

He lurched back to the pub door and fell through it, to the shouts of encouragement from his erstwhile drinking partners, and repeats of his punishment from the landlord.

A couple of minutes later he lurched back out, clutching two Woodbine packets, one containing a few cigarettes. ''Ere you are then; 'ow about these!' He staggered over to a lamppost and grabbed it for support. 'These'll get you goin',' he continued.

I took them without comment. Woodbine packets would add nothing to our collection; but the cigarettes had other possibilities.

We hung back for a couple of minutes, waiting for some further manifestation of his generosity. But time was going by. 'We'll 'ave to go now, Grandad, or we'll be late 'cause we 'ave to walk.' I made a last attempt, but Grandad was humming the opening bar of 'Danny Boy' as a prelude to vocalising it.

We set off to the strains of '...the pipes the pipes are call-all-in...' and got as far as the next corner, when, 'Wait-a-minute you lot, worrabout the tram fare?' Grandad broke off his rendition at the second verse.

We dashed back.

''Ow much is it?' he asked, still swaying backward and forward.

'Thri'pence each,' I replied. Last time it was a penny, but there might have been a fare increase.

''Ere we are then!' Grandad thrust his hand into his pockets, forgetting it was the one clutching the lamppost. He staggered a couple of yards into the road but managed to stay upright with the help of his boots.

''Ere we are then!' A handful of coins slipped from his fingers and rolled into the gutter. Five pairs of eager hands soon retrieved them. 'Is tharrenough?' he asked.

We carefully counted it out: tuppence-ha'penny, all in ha'pennies, and three farthings. 'It'll 'ave to do,' I replied, somewhat disappointed at the lack of silver. There was no point in pursuing the matter further. Grandad was clearing his throat.

We set off again, followed by Grandads raucous singing, '...across the glen an' up the mountin' side-a...'

After about five minutes we reached Upper Parliament Street, and made our way down towards the Rialto Ballroom. Upper Parliament Street was a wide road of once elegant townhouses, with impressive panelled doors set between fluted stone pillars. Now they were decaying: the rendering falling away in patches and the ancient paint flaking.

Many were not occupied, but some were. Their tenants sat on the top of front steps, chatting to passers-by and waving at the tramcars heading into town. Others were only occupied at night-time, when they made their livings on Lime Street.

At the crossroads of Upper and Lower Parliament Street stood the Rialto Ballroom. Five faces were pressed against the plate glass door, trying to work out what a Ballroom was. All we could see was a big door labelled 'Cloakroom', whatever that was, and a kiosk like the ones they had in the cinemas.

'It's where the nobs go to enjoy 'emselves,' stated Terry. 'An' the Yanks go at night-time to go dancing.'

Terry had overheard one of his American uncles trying to get his mam to go there for a dance. His mother had declined, saying that she would feel out of place, because it was 'For the nobs and not the likes of me.' Terry had put two and two together.

We lost interest. Dancing had something to do with girls.

Along Myrtle Street, past the Ear, Nose and Throat Hospital and down Leece Street to the city centre; we were in Church Street before the shops shut.

A chaos of clanging trams, goods-laden lorries and hordes of shoving, pushing, chattering people confronted us. It was noisy but exciting. The crowds ebbed and flowed between the rows of shops, a mass of busy people, but each knowing exactly where they were going.

We joined the throng, dodging and scurrying backwards and forwards between the lampposts and their litter bins. After about a quarter of an hour we sat down on the steps of Woolworth's to study our findings.

'Nothing but bloody Woodies and Capstans,' moaned Terry. 'What's up wiv 'em round 'ere; don't they know how to smoke or what?'

'I've gorra Wills packet,' volunteered Tommy.

'Ten or twenty?' I asked.

'Twenny,' answered Tommy.

''Ow about lerrin me 'ave it; I 'aven't got one an' it was my idea to come 'ere.' Tommy handed it over without a murmur.

Terry stood up and climbed to the top step. 'Worr'ave you done with Gimme Gimme?' he tapped Tommy on the shoulder.

Tommy's face went white.

In the excitement of the search, he had forgotten his charge. Montgomery was nowhere in sight!

'Montgomery, Montgomery, where 'ave you gone?' Tommy's voice quavered with trepidation. 'Montgomery, Montgomery!' Tommy stood on tiptoe scanning the bustling crowd. 'I'll 'ave to go an' find him.' Eyes wide with panic, he turned to us for help.

'You brought 'im, an' you lost 'im; so you can go an' bloody find 'im if you 'ave to; but if I was you I'd forgerrim … greedy little sod.' Billy was his usual helpful self.

Tommy's face was deathly white. He was desperate. The punishment metered out by his mother when he took Montgomery home late was bad enough. What was it going to be like if he didn't take him home at all?

'Will you help me please, Spud?' Tommy turned to me. 'If I go 'ome wivout 'im, me mam'll kill me; an' anyway 'e's only little an' 'e might get hurt.'

The idea of abandoning our search for cigarette packets in favour of a search for Montgomery, didn't appeal much. 'Someone will find 'im, don't worry,' I smiled reassuringly. 'Probably take 'im 'ome wiv them, and it might be someone rich.' My imagination began to take over. 'An' they'll keep 'im and look after 'im and buy 'im tons of toys for Christmas, and feed 'im.' At this point even my imagination gave up. Nobody would keep Gimme Gimme if they had to feed him!

Terry was in deep thought. He pointed over his shoulder into Woolworth's. 'He'll be in there, in Woollies, by the bloody sweet counter. I'll bet the greedy little sod's in there!'

'Thanks Terry,' there was adoration in Tommy's eyes. Now he had hope.

I knew from past experience that scruffy kids were not seen as valued customers by Woolworth's, and I doubted Terry was right. In any case the chances of us getting in to find out were so remote that we might as well forget about it.

Billy was on the same wavelength and was weighing up the chances of making a fast sortie to the sweet counter to see if Montgomery was there, followed by a dash for freedom.

Georgie, who had also been ejected from the store on more than one occasion, suggested a more logical approach that even Woolworth's management would accept.

'We'll just tell 'em we've lost Gimme Gimme an' we won't be a minute, an' they'll lerrus 'ave a look around. Anyway,' he added, 'I tell 'em if they don't lerrus take him out, they'll 'ave no bloody sweets left.'

There was no arguing with that logic, so Billy led the way through the great glass doors. We trooped in after him.

We entered a paradise for children. Row after row of glass-topped counters lay before us, almost, it seemed, as far as the eye could see. Row after row of everything imaginable: from toys to candles, from reels of cotton to pots and pans, from sweets to tools to more toys to more sweets; each section priced, with nothing more than sixpence.

We made it to the nearest sweet counter without being challenged. The long counter was divided by glass partitions separating small mountains of all kinds of sweets from Dolly Mixtures to Uncle Joe's, the end of each section labelled with its content's name and the price for a quarter and the price for two ounces.

A row of sweet jars stood on low shelves behind the small mountains; and wads of conical paper bags separated the jars. We stared open mouthed at paradise.

Terry's assessment of Montgomery's inner driving force was spot-on. Montgomery was standing at the middle of the sweet counter with up-stretched fingers, clinging to the glass upright, his fingertips twitching in a desperate attempt to reach into heaven. His face was beetroot-red with emotion and he breathed heavily from his exertion; but otherwise he was quiet, overcome by the overpowering feeling of being so near yet so far from all that he lived for. He couldn't even mouth 'gimme gimme'.

Tommy nearly passed out with relief when he saw him, but recovered quickly and grabbed Montgomery around the waist with both arms.

Desperate to escape with his charge, Tommy tried to haul Montgomery towards the exit. Montgomery's beetroot face suddenly blotched white with rage. Someone was trying to drag him away from paradise. Quiet determination turned to bellowing rage. Montgomery, still clinging to the top of the glass upright, was now horizontal and screaming.

'Gimme gimme!' he bellowed as Tommy pulled with all his might. But Montgomery hung on to paradise with a fierce strength, repeatedly demanding, 'Gimme gimme!' at the top of his voice.

Tommy's desperate hauling was irresistible but Montgomery was immovable. The glass upright was neither.

Tommy shot backwards at speed, as the upright parted company from the counter. Montgomery dropped to the floor, still clutching the glass. A mountain of sweets cascaded to the floor, burying Montgomery from the neck up and covering his arms.

Tommy headed backwards for the exit, still clasping his charge around the waist, hauling Gimme Gimme along the floor, with the glass upright acting like a scoop, bulldozing a mound of sweets behind them.

Montgomery stopped bellowing. It wasn't quite as good as before, but he was reasonably satisfied with the heap of sweets being dragged between his stretched arms and the glass. He allowed himself to be hauled silently towards the door, waiting for a dwell in the proceedings, before starting to shovel the heap into his mouth.

Tommy steadfastly strained backwards.

'What the 'ell do you think you're-a-doing?'

Tommy collided with a pair of polished black shoes. Not daring to let go of Montgomery, he had to bend his neck backwards to see who the shoes belonged to. A dark pin-striped suit towered over him, barring his way to freedom. It was the Store Manager.

Tommy looked about him for support, trembling with the combined effects of exertion and fear, but he was on his own. His friends and fellow ciggy-packet collectors were by then half way up Church Street.

'Bloody little thief!' The pin-striped suit's voice was pitched high with righteous indignation. 'I'm-a goin' to call the police!'

The mention of uniformed authority restored Tommy's instinct for self-preservation. The appearance of a policeman was often the forerunner to a clip around the ears from the bobby, followed later by another from his mam as word reached her about the first clip around the ears.

'We ain't doin' nothing, honest Mister. We was only collectin' ciggy packets, Mister, an' I forgorrabout him.' Tommy nodded at Montgomery, who had taken full advantage of the halt and was shovelling sweets into his mouth. 'An' 'e ain't done nothin' wrong' honest Mister, an' I've gotta take 'im 'ome now,' Tommy continued, hoping against hope that whoever was in the black shoes had not noticed the fast disappearing mound of sweets.

'You're-a going nowhere,' stated the pin-striped suit. 'You are-a pinching them sweets, and he's wolfing them down right in front of me, cheeky little sod, so I'm-a going to get a policeman and 'ave you locked up.'

Tommy's voice rose an octave at the repeated threat. 'It was anaxident, honest. The shelf fell down an' all the sweets gorrin the way of 'is hands.'

The sight of a barefoot urchin clasping a smaller urchin round the waist and dragging him head down through a trail of sweets, had begun to attract quite an audience. One or two of the onlookers were investigating the trail of sweets. The pin-striped suit decided action was called for. He grabbed Tommy by the hair then advised the audience to stop investigating the sweets because they were the property of Woolworth Stores Ltd.

He tightened his grip on Tommy's head. Tommy winced with pain, but his hold on Montgomery never faltered.

'Lerrim go, you miserable sod!' A burly, red faced, man thrust his way through the audience. He confronted the pin-striped suit, legs apart in muddied wellington boots, dressed in a grubby vest with no shirt. He was chewing a mouthful of Woolworth's 'Delicious Everton Toffees'.

'Lerrim go you miserable bugger! 'E's doin' no 'arm is 'e? Worrarm 'is 'e doin'?'

'No harm, no harm!' the pin-striped suit retorted, in disbelief. 'No harm! Of course he's-a doing harm, he's-a pinching sweets, that's what he's-a doing,' he continued sternly, 'and I'm the Manager!' The Manager waited for the full impact of his authority to take effect.

'I don't care if you're Jesus bloody Christ! Lerrim go or I'll stick one on yer.' The red-faced man was obviously not impressed by the status of the pin-striped suit, but the pin-striped suit seemed to be quite impressed with the man in a grubby vest. He immediately let go of Tommy's hair.

Tommy seized his chance and let go of Montgomery's waist with the idea of them heading for safety on four feet. But Montgomery stayed flat out on the floor, continuing to stuff sweets into his mouth until his cheeks were bulging. With no room left in his mouth, he stuffed them down his shirt-front.

The Manager decided to try and make the best of a worsening situation. He started to pick up the remaining sweets, summoning assistance with a practiced twitch of his finger.

Montgomery saw what he was up to and bellowed the only words he knew. 'Gimme gimme! Gimme gimme!' The noise coming from such a diminutive figure was impressive.

Even the red-faced man was impressed. He stooped down, patted Montgomery's half buried head, then disappeared into the audience, his mouth and his trouser pockets bulging.

Tommy saw his protector going and snatched Montgomery by the hand, dragging him towards the door. The pinstriped suit tried to grab them but stumbled and fell over someone's outstretched foot. Tommy had another, but anonymous, protector.

Once outside, Tommy kept going and eventually caught up with us at the top of Church Street; with Montgomery still in tow, steadily transferring sweets from down his shirt to down his mouth. Gimme Gimme's tenacity had to be admired for one so young. He had managed to hold on to at least half a pound of mixed toffees.

We sat on the steps of a closed solicitor's office.

'Well go on then; share 'em out,' I demanded. ''E wouldn't 'ave 'ad them if it wasn't for me lerrin you come.'

Tommy made a half hearted attempt to dig some of the sweets out of Montgomery's vice like grip. Montgomery bellowed and Tommy hurriedly let go, having only managed to wrest two from the grip.

'For Christ's sake shut 'im up will you, we'll all get caught if you don't shut 'im up. Tell 'im 'e can keep 'is bloody sweets, greedy sod.'

In the end, psychology triumphed. Georgie undid the paper on the two toffees. Gimme gimme's mouth was so full he couldn't fully close it and Georgie stuffed the unwrapped sweets through the half-open jaws.

Montgomery was silenced again, his taste buds over-stimulated by eating toffees without the wrappers on them.

Georgie hauled Montgomery's shirt out of his pants and half a pound of toffees cascaded down the steps. 'One for you, one for you, one for me, one for...' We shared out the sweets.

It was then we realised Billy was missing.

''E must still be in Woolies,' George said. 'Serves 'im right if 'e ends up in bloody jail.'

The prospect of seeing Billy marched off to the cooler overcame any apprehension we had, and we retraced our steps. We stood on tiptoe, our faces flattened against the great plate glass windows; but there was no sign of Billy.

Terry surveyed the goodies stretched out before him. 'I'll go in an' 'ave a look,' he volunteered, with a strange but determined look on his face. With that he stepped behind a smartly dressed couple linking arms, and followed them through the door.

Terry's ploy worked, though I was not sure whether he was hiding behind the couple or pretending to be their son. I hoped, for Terry's sake, he was hiding: they wouldn't mind that; but I suspected they would take great exception to a scruffy kid with holes in his socks pretending to be related to them.

Terry made it to the first counter without being challenged.

'Where the 'ell 'ave you lot been? I've been lookin' for you. Let's gerrout of 'ere quick for Christ's sake!' Billy suddenly appeared behind us.

The wild look in Billy's eyes said he'd done something he shouldn't have done; and joining him in his attempt to escape from whatever it was might make me an accessory.

'We can't,' I replied. 'We'll 'ave to wait for Terry, he's gone in Woolies lookin' for you.'

The wild stare in Billy's eyes grew wilder. 'Well I'm buggerin' off. I'm goin' to the Pier 'Ead. Tarar, I'll see you there.' Billy peered through the window, scanning the crowds in Woolworth's, then glanced anxiously over his shoulder. Apparently satisfied, he ran like the wind up Church Street, dodging between prams and people, and shouting back: 'By the Birken'ead ferry!'

We pressed our faces back on the window; but there was no sign of Terry.

Suddenly there was a commotion at another entrance. Terry erupted through it running at full pelt, with the pin-striped suit in hot pursuit. 'Stop 'im! Stop the little sod, he's a thief, stop him!'

A few people stopped to get a better view, but nobody reacted to the Manager's plea. There was nothing very special about being a thief in Woolies; most people had been one at one time or another.

Terry dodged and weaved amongst the shoppers, hardly faltering in his flight up Church Street. The Manager was not as skillful. He collided with a large woman carrying an enormous shopping bag, bounced off and stumbled into the back of the red-faced man in a vest.

'Oy, you! Bloody-'ell, it's you isn' it! What the sodden 'ell d'you fink you're doin'. You tryin' to be funny or what?'

WOOLWORTHS

...everything imaginable: from toys to candles, from reels of cotton to pots and pans, from sweets to tools to more toys to more sweets: with nothing more than sixpence

The red-faced man grabbed him by the collar of his pin-striped suit. 'What's up wiv you, callin' the police for kids who 'ave done nothin' an' nearly knockin' me over. Are you barmy or somethin'?'

The manager struggled in vain to back away. The large lady waddled over and thrust her shopping bag into his face. ''E nearly sodden-well knocked me over as well, 'e did.' She turned to the red-faced man.

The red-faced man blanched at the sight of the sheer bulk of the lady with the shopping bag, and hurriedly let go of the pin-striped suit. 'You are bloody barmy, you are!'

The manager retrieved his head from the shopping bag and ran back into the safety of his emporium. One or two of Woolworth's customers had noticed his temporary absence and were steadily chewing their way through a selection of the store's offerings. The immediate excitement over, we set off to find Terry and Billy.

'You go over on that side, and we'll stay on this side; an' make sure we don't miss 'em.' I instructed Georgie to walk on the other side of Lord Street, as we made our way up the slight hill towards the Pier Head.

We found Terry sitting on the pavement edge underneath the Victoria Monument perched on the top of the hill. Her Majesty surveyed the bustling city as far as Woolies, but Terry was sitting behind her back looking down at the grey expanse of the River Mersey. He was clutching something in his hand: it was a bar of Lifebuoy soap.

'Where'd you gerrit?' I sat down beside him as the others straggled up towards us.

Terry turned the bar over in his hand. 'Sort of seemed to come into me 'and.' He turned the soap over and over as though he wasn't sure he liked its unfamiliar touch. 'Sort of seemed to stick to me hand when I picked it up to 'ave a look at it.'

We were baffled. We all knew the temptations of Woolworth's shelves, piled high with sweets and toys; but Terry had stolen a bar of soap! He never touched the stuff at home so why...?

Georgie interrupted my thoughts. 'Worra you gunna do wiv it; it's no bloody good is it?' It was more a statement than a question.

'Worram I gunna do wiv it? Worram I gunna do wiv it? Worra you think I'm gonna do wiv it? I'm gonna bloody keep it, that's what I'm gonna bloody do wiv it; worrelse do you think I'm gonna do wiv it?' Terry had risked his all for the prize, so to him it had a value nothing to do with its usefulness. 'I'm gonna purrit wiv me other things when I get home. Anyway I can give it to me mam for Christmas,' he added, in a flash of inspiration.

Georgie had to admit it might be useful after all. Our mothers seemed to attach great importance to bars of soap, and his was forever trying to get him to share her liking for it.

He had to admit, it was better than the present he had given to his mother last Christmas: two Sunday School lesson cards and a candle from St Bernard's. Whatever appeal they might have had was lost when Billy advised his mother that, 'You're supposed to pay Jesus a penny for a candle, aren't you mam? But 'e didn't, 'e wont go to 'eaven, 'e waited till Father Bunloaf wasn't lookin', an' nicked it.'

Whilst there was still a bit of a question as to why it was a bar of soap and not a Dinky car or some other valuable, Terry became the hero of the day. Woolworth's was full of desirables, all beyond our financial means. All we had done was stare through the window at them, but here was Terry: he had stared at them too, but unlike us, he had gone in and helped himself, scornful of his lack of funds. He had dared, and he had won.

We gave Terry three cheers in the time honoured fashion and set off again, this time to find Billy.

Terry made the most of his newfound status. He walked ahead of us with a pronounced swagger, one hand stuffed in his pocket and the other brandishing the bar of Lifebuoy Soap. We dodged the horse-drawn wagons and steam-driven trucks rumbling along the Dock Road between ships and warehouses, and reached the cast-iron structure of the overhead railway, just as a train with its wooden carriages rattled above our craned faces.

'I've been on that,' I announced, 'twice!'

Terry stopped dead in his tracks. 'When?' he demanded, suspicious that I might be diverting attention from his heroic image.

'Once wiv me Grandad who knows someone as drives 'em and once wiv me Uncle Charlie, when 'e got back on leave from Africa,' I insisted.

They believed me. Uncle Charlie was the only real hero we knew. All the others were known only through the pages of our comics, but Uncle Charlie was flesh and blood, particularly blood. The last time we saw him was only a couple of months ago.

We were in my Grandma Nin's house when Uncle Charlie arrived home on leave from the Army. Uncle Charlie sat on his kit-bag in Nin's backyard and gathered us around him.

''Ow many Germans 'ave you killed?' Billy asked the question on all our lips.

He advised us that he couldn't tell us everything, because he'd promised Field Marshal Montgomery not to give away too many secrets. However, he could tell us that he had been fighting in Africa.

He then regaled us with stories of his hair-raising feats: sorting out the Nazis in the desert, by shooting thousands and seeing off the rest with hand to hand fighting. To prove the point he produced a German Army bayonet from his kit bag and two African knives which, he assured us, had been used for collecting ingredients for the dinners of a tribe of head-hunting cannibals.

Uncle Charlie told us the knives were presented to him, by the Tribal Chief, in recognition for his bravery in killing a pride of lions that had consumed most of his subjects. They turned out to be a very useful present. He used them, as the only weapons he had at the time, to see off dozens of Panzers with machine guns, and hundreds of SS troops with bayonets on the end of their rifles.

To put any doubts about his single-handed desert campaign to bed, he showed us how the bayonet was shiny bright, whereas his African knives were stained brown with the dried blood of whole battalions of the enemy.

Billy had examined the knives with loving interest and gave Uncle Charlie his full support. 'It's bloody blood alright,' he pronounced. Billy knew about these things so any thought that it might have been rust, was ridiculous.

Nin had interrupted Uncle Charlie just as he was explaining how to get a knife out once you'd stuck it in. She clipped Rommel's victor round the ears, told him not to frighten the children, then hauled him indoors by the scruff of his neck.

'Is your Uncle Charlie comin' 'ome again soon?' Georgie inquired. ''cause if 'e is...'

'Never mind 'is Uncle bloody Charlie, worrabout Billy?' Terry interrupted, his hero image dented by the memory of Uncle Charlie. 'Come on,
let's see if 'e's down by the landin' stage.

We ran under the railway and crossed the road to the side of the Liver
Building, then down to the waterfront.

The grey-brown mass of the River Mersey looked heavier than water, as
it swirled in sluggish eddies around the great wooden structure supporting
the walkways at the Pier Head. The smell of seawater and tarred wood; the
smoke from the ferries; the busy small boats; tugs cajoling ships to their
moorings; this was the Pier Head.

It was more than a place, it was the lifeblood of our city: the port that
saw the departure of the great Atlantic Merchant fleets in the war years
and a home for those that survived. Our Pier Head was not a place, it was
an atmosphere; and we loved it.

Uncle Charlie was forgotten and so too was Billy.

We ran along the granite-paved high waterfront to the wood-lined
tunnels that led to the lower waterfront: the floating platforms that were
the ferry landing stages. The tunnels were suspended on massive iron
hinges at both ends, subservient to the ebb and flow of the Mersey's great
tides. If you got it right, you could make the suspended tunnel vibrate to
stamping feet.

'Right, gerrin line then!' I arranged Georgie, Terry and Tommy in a row,
with Gimme Gimme on Tommy's shoulder. We tramped down the tunnel,
line abreast, stamping our feet in strict time.

Woompt! Woompt! Woompt! The whole structure resonated under our
pounding feet. Woompt! Woompt! Woompt!

'Bloody great that, we'll 'ave another go!' But I was talking to myself;
the others were lined up along the water's edge, surveying the expanse of
Liverpool's Dockland.

Birkenhead and the cranes of Cammell Laird's Shipyard could be seen
over the far side of the river, right opposite; but even more exciting, you
could make out the pier and Tower Ballroom at the seaside resort of New
Brighton, way over to the west.

The tide was still rising, flooding the river far upstream, beyond Garston
Docks and onwards towards Hale, Runcorn and Warrington: distant places
to Liverpudlians.

The ferries were busy ploughing the waters between The Pool, Seacombe,
Birkenhead and New Brighton. The most famous of all, the *Royal Daffodil*,
had disgorged its passengers for Liverpool and was about to return to
Birkenhead.

We watched the last few passengers boarding the *Daffodil* by the wide gangplank to the lower deck, whilst a couple of the crew were on the landing stage hauling up the smaller gangplank that served the upper deck. The engines grumbled and the water churned creamy brown as the boat swung about, and headed over the river.

We waved and cheered to the passengers, and they waved back. It seemed the natural thing to do: to cheer the travellers onwards, to the land across the Mersey. We watched the boat until it was half way across, then turned back to survey the crowds on the landing stage. The only barrier between the edge of the landing stage and the river was an iron chain hung between fluted cast iron posts.

Tommy balanced Montgomery on the chain and, holding him firmly, pushed him gently to and fro.

Georgie stood up. 'Can 'e swim?' he asked.

'No 'e bloody-well can't,' Tommy replied, hurriedly swinging

PIER HEAD FERRY

We ran along the granite-paved high waterfront to the wood-lined tunnels that led to the lower waterfront: the floating platforms that were the ferry landing stages

Montgomery back onto terra firma. He was not quite sure what Georgie had in mind when he asked the question, but it was better to be safe than sorry.

'Hey, look-a' this.' Terry ran to the now upended gangplank under the sign 'Birkenhead Ferry', and stooped down to pick something up. He rejoined us. 'Look a' this! Three Castles, an' I 'aven't got one!' Terry gloated over the empty green cigarette packet.

We were suddenly reminded of what we'd come for: cigarette packets and Billy. A mad scramble to the litter bins produced the usual abundance of Woody packets, together with two Craven 'A' and a Wills No. 3.

'Well at least we've gorra few,' Terry stated.

Georgie didn't answer, he'd found nothing. 'Where's our bloody Billy gone?' he reminded us of our other quest, ''e said 'e'd be by the Birken'ead Ferry an' 'e's norrere.'

'Maybe 'e meant the New Brighton one,' I suggested. But that was only a few yards away, and there was no sign of him there either. I was about to suggest that Billy might have fallen off the landing stage and drowned, when out of one of the tunnels sauntered Billy; his head was enveloped in a cloud of smoke.

He swaggered towards us and casually plucked the smoking cigarette from his lips. 'Turkish,' he said, and put it back in.

We just stood and stared, open-mouthed. Even Gimme Gimme seemed to take interest, and stopped chewing for a few seconds. Billy took a long draw of the cigarette and coughed out a great cloud of smoke at us.

Tommy's mouth dropped open.

Georgie stared in disbelief.

'Bloody sodden 'ell, where d'you gerrit?' Terry managed to blurt out.

Billy carefully set the cigarette between his two first fingers, plucked it from his lips with a sweeping flourish and held it above his shoulder with palm outstretched; just like they did in films.

'Woolies,' he replied, nonchalantly. 'Gorrem from Woolies wiv these.' He pulled a box of Swan Vestas from his shirt-front, then delved back in to produce a packet of ten Abdullah cigarettes, 'Made in Turkey'.

Georgie looked around, surveying the crowds for pin-striped suits. 'Jesus Christ, Billy; you've 'ad it! You've gone an' bloody done it now you 'ave! Sodden 'ell, we'll all go to bloody jail now, we will. You rotten sod!'

I was beginning to think it was getting a bit late and it might be an idea if I left the others and went home, fast. Terry toyed with the bar of Lifebuoy. Georgie might be right about Billy's fate; and the same might apply to those with bars of soap. Flight seemed the only solution. Tommy was already heading off with the still silent Gimme Gimme.

Billy must have sensed he would soon be on his own.

'I gorrem for everyone you know. You don't think I only gorrem for me, do you? Billy said, indignantly. Don't you wan' any, or what? Thought we came 'ere for cigarette packets an' I got a rare un an' I was gonna share the ciggies wiv you,' he continued.

It was then I remembered the half-full packet of Woodies, donated by Grandad. I fished them out of my pocket: there were five. 'I've got me own.' I showed Billy the cigarettes, satisfied that I could flee with a clear conscience.

Billy looked at them with scorn in his eyes. 'Woodbines, bloody old Woodies. These are Abdullah's Turkey ones; these are real ciggies not like them bloody things. Anyway, do you want one or not?'

Georgie reconsidered the position. Usually, whatever punishment Billy suffered, Billy made sure Georgie suffered at least the same. If Georgie was not careful he'd end up with all of the pain and none of the pleasure. If he was going to jail, he decided, he'd go for good reason. 'I'll 'ave one,' he said.

Tommy rejoined us and we all stretched out our hands. Billy doled out a cigarette each.

'An' we'll 'ave one of yours too,' Georgie turned accusingly to me. I doled out a Woodbine each. 'An' we'll 'ave another one from you too,' Georgie turned defiantly to Billy. Billy somewhat reluctantly handed out the last of his Abdullahs. We each had three cigarettes except Billy who had two, and a half smoked one.

'Gis a light.' Georgie puckered his lips round a cigarette and leaned up to Billy's smoking Abdullah.

A couple of minutes later we stood in a ring, admiring each other's expertise at taking the fags from our lips, and replacing them with a careless twist of the wrist.

'Right then, I votes we go 'ome now,' I tried speaking with the cigarette dangling from my lips, just like Dick Tracy. The cigarette fell out and I stepped on it. 'Look at that! Bloody thing wasn't made prop'ly an' it fell out.'

The others agreed with me. They were experiencing similar difficulties in keeping control of the Abdullahs, that apart from their coughing. We swaggered back up the tunnels and across the square towards the Liver Buildings.

Billy stopped in front of the splendid building. 'Not real, them up there you know,' Billy pointed up to the two great bronze statues of mythical birds perched on the top of the Liver Building. 'Them's called Liver Birds and they're used by sailors when they come in 'ere so they know they're in Liverpool. Otherwise they wouldn't know where they were 'cause they've been away to sea for years and years, an' when they cum in they've no idea where they are, so they look up 'ere an' when they see the Liver Birds, they knows where they are.'

We stared up at Liverpool's famous landmark through a haze of cigarette smoke. Billy's story seemed entirely reasonable to me. 'What are they then, if they're not real uns?' I asked.

Billy paused in deep thought. 'Miss ... missa ... misslog ... missalogical ones,' stated Billy, flourishing his fag in the direction of the statues. 'Them's missalogical ones; dead missalogical ones.'

And that seemed entirely reasonable too.

'Worrappens if the sailors come 'ere an' look up, an' see the Liver Birds, but they don't wanna be 'ere?' Terry inquired.

Billy struggled with that thought for a couple of minutes. 'Well they get back in their bloody ships and sod off somewhere else, don't they. Anyway, if they didn' wanna come 'ere, what the sodden 'ell did they come 'ere for in the first place?'

There was no good answer to that, so Terry changed the question. 'Worrappens if the sailors go somewhere else an' look up an' don't see the Liver Birds, but they wanna be 'ere?' he asked.

Billy was becoming exasperated. 'Well they get back in their bloody ships an' sod off again from wherever they are; an' they come 'ere an' look up an' see the Liver Birds an' knows they're 'ere don't they. Anyway if they didn' wanna be somewhere else, what the sodden 'ell did they go there for in the first place then? Are you bloody stupid or something?'

Terry didn't answer, deciding to let the matter rest. Billy was probably right, they shouldn't go away to sea if they didn't know where they were sailing to.

The discussion seemed pointless to me. I'd never seen any sailors looking up at the Liver Building anyway. The only ones I'd ever seen were chatting ten to the dozen to women on the street corners along Lime Street, and they seemed to know exactly where they were going.

Tommy and I sauntered on and the others caught up with us half way along Lord Street. One or two of the more upright citizens of Liverpool made passing comments as we dodged through the crowds of shoppers, a pall of smoke following us at head level.

'Just look at those children, absolutely disgraceful!' a tall thin lady observed to her taller, thinner husband, 'I don't know what's wrong with the children of today.' Then, in a flash of inspiration, she discovered the reason for our delinquency, and that of all children from Adam and Eve onward. 'I blame their parents!' she stated, emphatically.

The comments were lost on us as we rummaged through the litter bins, adding a few new additions to our collection by the time we crossed

Paradise Street. We struggled to an untidy halt and sat down on the pavement in the alley alongside Coopers. The rich tangy smell of coffee, for which the store was famous, pervaded the air all around us, except the area occupied by our cloud of cigarette smoke.

'I'm not goin' past Woolies,' Terry stated emphatically. We all agreed. It was decided that the best plan would be to go along Paradise Street, down to the Dingle, through Prince's Park, then back along Alt Street.

'Look a' that!' Billy tapped his smoking fag to form a dot in the centre of a perfectly blown smoke-ring. We all set about blowing smoke rings. Much puffing and blowing produced a few distorted shapes; but only Billy had mastered the art.

Our efforts devoured the second of our fags, so we lit the third. Funny things were beginning to happen at the back of my throat and in my tummy, but I persevered. 'That's norra bad one,' I wheezed, as a ragged circle of smoke formed above my head.

'Norras good as mine,' George countered, faintly, his face a peculiar shade of grey.

Billy blew one ring after the other, ignoring our amateurish attempts.

Tommy gave up trying and offered his remaining Abdullah. 'Don't think I like this smoking much,' he observed. 'Me mouth's all 'orrible an' me guts is funny.'

Billy grabbed the proffered fag. 'It's up to you; burrit's bloody great, look at that!' He produced another perfect ring.

By the time I was well down on my third cigarette and Billy on his fourth, I felt decidedly ill.

'What's up wiv you lot?' Billy asked. 'Jesus Christ, you've gone all white … and you 'ave … an' you 'ave … an' you!' He glanced from one to the other. 'What's up wiv you?' We couldn't answer; we were all going to die; or if we weren't, we hoped we would.

'I'm gonna be sick,' Georgie stated, as a matter of fact rather than opinion.

'So am I,' I agreed faintly.

'And me too,' Terry concurred.

Tommy hastily pulled Gimme Gimme out of range.

'Well you better hadn't spew up over me; you'll purrout me ciggy,' Billy allowed the fag to dangle professionally from his lips as he spoke, then licked it back into place and continued blowing perfect rings.

We fell silent as the tobacco smoke did its worst to our insides. The world in front of us had disappeared in a fog of sickly grey smoke, slowly swirling around our heads. We were only dimly aware of the world outside the haze of smoke, but gradually, in the grey swirling mist, a face materialised: a face with a moustache on it.

The apparition crystallising from the smoke began to assume the shape of some one we knew. I had a vague notion that it might be Saint Peter welcoming us through the Gates of Heaven to a place where nobody had aching throats or sickly tummies: to a place were smoking was forbidden.

But as the vague shape took form, we began to realise it might not be Saint Peter after all. In fact it began to assume the features of Pop Bath, our teacher. He was no saint, he wouldn't be allowed in heaven, so it must be the other place we were going to. I didn't mind one bit, anywhere was better than here on earth.

Billy seemed oblivious to the apparition, and puffed his biggest and best smoke-ring yet. It drifted from his lips to fit perfectly around the moustached apparition, then hovered for a few seconds before disappearing up the nostrils above the moustache.

The apparition then spoke. 'It is you, isn't it? It had to be you, didn't it? And I might have known who would be with you!'

The awful truth slowly dawned on me. We weren't in heaven after all; we weren't even in hell. It was worse than that. We were still on earth, in the presence of someone more powerful and fearful than all the Gods: our teacher from Tiber Street County School, Pop Bath.

His face was three inches from mine, the precise distance adopted by him in school, just before punishment was meted out. In fact we only knew Pop Bath from three distances: as far away as we could get; three inches; and two foot behind us with a cane in his hand. We were at phase two of the distances and this was usually followed by phase three: the two foot one.

'Where did you get those cigarettes from?' He continued the measured tone. 'I want the truth from you, none of your lies. Do you understand?'

The demand sounded ominously like the one a judge had made in a play on the wireless last Saturday. The play ended with the person being questioned getting hanged. None of us could answer; we were paralysed with fear. Even Billy had frozen into silence, with the remains of his last Abdullah hanging from his lips.

'No matter,' he continued, 'we shall find out when you get back to school. I would like you to report to my office, on Monday, before assembly.'

The word 'like' offered some hope. Maybe we had an option; but then: 'Give me any cigarettes you have and report to me immediately you return to school.' Hope faded: we had no option.

'Take that out of your mouth, immediately!' Pop Bath switched his three-inch distance from me to Billy. It was too late. Billy screamed as the burning end of the fag reached his upper lip. His mouth dropped open and the still lit fag dropped off his lip into his mouth. Billy screamed again and sprang to his feet, jumping up and down, frantically huffing and puffing, trying desperately to eject the instrument of torture.

The spittle-soaked butt shot out, straight into Pop Bath's eye.

The teacher did not allow even a blink, but with measured care took a white folded handkerchief from his top pocket, wiped the spit from his eye and returned to the three-inch position. He stared fixedly at Billy, but addressed all of us. 'I won't ask again,' he stated. 'Give me any cigarettes you have, immediately!'

Billy stared with wild-eyed unseeing panic. His mouth was still wide open, but the distance between his lips grew smaller as his scorched top lip swelled to meet the bottom one.

Tommy decided the whole thing had nothing to do with him. He had already packed up smoking and as such was safe from any possible retribution. He decided he would try to help his mates who still had the habit.

'They 'aven't gorrany left, Sir,' he volunteered. 'They've smoked all the ones they 'ad an' the ones as I gave 'em when I packed up smoking. They didn't 'ave many because Spud's grandad only gave him five and Terry nicked a bar of Lifebuoy from Woolies instead of ciggies, and the packet of Turkey ones that Billy nicked only had ten in it.'

Billy's eyes glazed as the hopelessness of his position overwhelmed him. Terry, Georgie and me were beyond words too: overwhelmed by the awful presence of the teacher, the effect of tobacco smoke on our innards, but most of all by Tommy's unselfish attempt to save us.

It was Sunday tomorrow, and the day after was Monday: back to school day. Before assembly, Mr Bath took up the two-foot position behind each of us in turn. As a result, we couldn't sit down for the rest of the day.

Much the same position was taken up by our various mothers, after the Headmistress advised them by letter that our teacher had taken up his two foot position because of his interest in our future wellbeing.

Billy and Georgie's mother was so worried about their wellbeing that she had to have a cigarette to calm her nerves, after she had read the letter. Georgie watched the smoke curling up from her lips, his stomach churning as he caught a whiff of the blue-grey haze. Billy watched too, waiting to see where his mother would leave the fag end when she finished with it.

Later in the week, when memories began to fade, we gathered in the backyard of No. 43, surrounded by our extended collection of cigarette packets.

'Where's your Turkey one?' Terry inquired, surveying Billy's array.

Billy looked around for any sign of my mother. 'Buried it,' he whispered, 'buried it on the debbie, so's nobody'll know where I gorrit.'

It seemed to me that this was a bit like bolting the stable door, with the horse disappearing over the horizon. Billy had been punished twice from the two-foot position: once for smoking cigarettes and once for stealing them.

'Whereabouts?' Georgie asked.

'Mind your own bloody business,' Billy muttered. 'I buried it an' its staying buried; an' you can forgerrabout it; an' I'll bury anyone as tries to dig it up.'

Georgie decided to forget about it. Some swapping of duplicate packets followed the usual haggling, but we soon got fed up. Terry's suggestion to go looking for more was ignored.

We fell into a despondent silence, interrupted by Tommy as he suddenly remembered his responsibilities. Tommy got up and went out into the jigger to make sure Gimme Gimme had enough Woody packets to eat. He only had one left, so Tommy gave him a valuable Craven 'A' and a Capstan Full Strength. After all, he was his little brother.

'Where's your mam?' Billy asked.

'Gone shopping,' I replied. 'Why?'

Billy ignored the question. 'How long'll she be?' he inquired.

'She's gone for spuds with Mrs Callaghan, and then she's goin' to the chippy. She'll be hours, why?'

Billy again ignored the question, and pulled out a Capstan Full Strength packet from his shirtfront, then a box of matches from his pocket. He flipped open the lip of the packet and tipped its contents onto the tiles: six or seven cigarette ends. 'I'm gonna make a fag,' he announced.

Georgie turned a pale green, the back of my throat went dry and Terry doubled up in a fit of coughing.

Tommy came back in and saw the little mound of cigarette ends. 'I know 'ow to roll your own, you know,' he advised Billy. 'Me bruvver does it. 'E buys cigarette papers from Mottram's an' rolls 'is own.'

'I know 'ow to do it meself,' Billy retorted. 'Only I 'aven't gorrany ciggy papers.'

Tommy went over to the bin mounted on the wall of the jigger, and rummaged through its contents. 'There's an old *Echo* in 'ere,' he announced. 'Can Billy borrow a birrovit to roll 'is own?' He retrieved a page from the newspaper that hadn't been used for the budgie's cage and handed it to Billy. 'Don't roll one for me Billy, 'cause I've packed in smokin'.'

The rest of us watched the proceedings as terrible memories of churning stomachs and teachers at three-inch and two-foot distances came racing back to mind.

Billy tore off a piece, about the length of a cigarette, and carefully pulled apart his collection of fag ends; emptying the remains of their tobacco into the fragment of *Echo*. After much rolling and teasing, he held out a thin tube of paper for inspection. The tube of loosely rolled paper contained a few shreds of tobacco.

'Norras good as a Turkey one, but not bad issit!' he pronounced. He placed the makeshift fag carefully between his lips and struck a match.

We watched in glum silence, expecting the moustached apparition to appear at any moment. As soon as Billy was sure of our full attention, he applied the lighted match to his ciggy; his eyes half-closed in anticipation of the first cigarette of the day.

He took a long deep draw.

Billy screamed. The flame from the match consumed the fag in an instant, right down to his upper lip. His mouth dropped open and he screamed again as the flaming remains dropped into his mouth.

Billy sprang to his feet and jumped up and down, huffing and puffing, trying desperately to eject the instrument of torture. But all that came out was bits of charred paper. Billy's scorched lips closed together as the swelling spread.

I got up and went into the house, leaving the others to their own devices, and went upstairs to find Charlie's stamp collection. I flicked through his album, carefully removing any stamps where there was a duplicate.

Charlie had dozens with the same picture on them, even though they were different colours and different amounts. Ten minutes later I had quite a good selection.

Collecting cigarette packets was, I decided, a painful and unhealthy pastime. Stamp collecting might not be as interesting, but I'd never seen Pop Bath's face three inches from Charlie's; and collecting stamps, as far as I knew, had no effect on Charlie's stomach, or his ability to sit down.

The Masked Avengers

'Chuck 'er in the nettles, for Christ sake! ... Chuck 'im in, then chuck 'er in, an' chuck that bloody doll in as well!'

If you prick us, do we not bleed? ... if you poison us, do we not die? and if you wrong us, shall we not revenge?

The Merchant of Venice, William Shakespeare

IT WAS YET ANOTHER BORING, hot sunny day near the end of school summer holidays, and we had gathered in Billy and Georgie's backyard, stuck for something to do.

Billy was trying to catch a fly to put on a spider's web he had discovered behind the mangle. He gave up and clouted his brother Georgie over the head. 'If you hadn't 'ave moved, I'd 'ave 'ad that one! Blummin idiot!'

Georgie didn't seem to notice. Clouts over the head from Billy were just one of life's little routines.

'Just too bloody many of 'em.' Terry stood up and examined the spider's web. 'Norrenough room; they just gerrin the way all the time,' he continued.

'What d'you mean, too many? There was only one, an' I missed it 'cause 'e bloody-well moved.' Billy threatened Georgie with another clout.

'Not flies, I'm not talkin' about sodden flies am I?' said Terry, exasperated. 'It's people I'm talkin' about, too many people. It's the sodden people in Sevvy Park, what I'm talkin' about, aren't I? Christ, who cares 'ow many flies there is?' Terry poked the web to emphasise his point.

He was right of course. Sefton Park was always crowded, particularly at weekends. Hundreds of mothers and dozens of obedient dads shoved prams bulging with screaming babies hurling out ice creams and teething rings, moaning at us for not keeping off the grass.

Sefton Park entrance

But worse than that were the

174

free-ranging kids, particularly the girls. Gangs of them rampaged across the fields, climbing our trees, getting in the way with their 'ring-a-ring of roses' and other ridiculous games, always in the firing line of our arrows, or right in the middle of our cricket pitch, or feeding the ducks whilst we were trying to fish.

We got no peace even when the light began to fade. Our serious attempts to emulate Robin Hood were constantly disrupted as we fell over older boys and girls playing doctors and nurses.

Terry was right. Sefton Park was overcrowded.

We made our way down the tree-lined avenue, towards the sound of music.

The Liverpool Constabulary Brass Band was in full swing on the bandstand, on the island in our favourite fishing lake, just past the café. Their audience spilled over from the seats around the bandstand, to the lawns surrounding the lake.

Toddlers in baggy nappies staggered erratic courses through the crowd, stumbling over prostrate music lovers, watched by their adoring mothers and followed nose-to-nappy by appreciative dogs.

The end of each rendition from the band was greeted by enthusiastic clapping, together with a variety of suggestions.

'Eh Scuffer, play anuvver one so I can go an' rob a bank!' 'Aww, sodden-'ell, don't play any more, we 'aven't done nothing wrong!'

There were hundreds of people, further proof of Terry's claim.

Just along the path, leading away from the band and past Eros Fountain, stood the Open Air Theatre: the first venue for Scousers intent on a career of international stardom.

It featured jugglers, striving to be different from their co-stars, by hurling all kinds of bizarre objects into the air and catching the odd one or two. Magicians in faded lumpy evening suits mesmerised their audience of small children and pensioners every Saturday and Bank Holidays by producing miles of tied-together grubby multi-coloured handkerchiefs out of thin air.

We had stopped to see a show a few weeks ago, featuring an elderly gentleman singing 'Eskimo Nell'. Despite there being nothing on today, a crowd of people were leaning on the railings, gawping at the stage.

'Look a'them all, wouldn't mind if they were reg'lers like us,' Terry muttered, 'they only come 'ere when it's sunny, specially the bloody girls, ring-a-ring-a-rosin' it all over the bloody place, when we're tryin' to play prop'ly. Just gerrin in the way, ring-a-ring-a-bloody-rosin'. An' worrare they doin' in the bushes anyway? Worrappens in doctors an' nurses? Seems to me they're just lyin' about an' lookin' at each other, gerrin in the way. Anyway worrappens in doctors an' nurses?'

'Aw shurrup!' Georgie interrupted Terry's discourse. 'There's nothin' you can do about it, so shurrup.'

'Don't be too sure about that,' Terry muttered darkly. 'Don't be so blummin sure.'

The next day, we continued our bored discussion in Billy and Georgie's backyard.

'Where is Nottingham anyway? It's norrin England.' Billy's England ended somewhere near Birkenhead, on the other side of the Mersey.

'It is in England!' Georgie retorted. 'It's near Sherwood Forest where 'e's buried under a great big oak tree. He shot an arrow wiv 'is longbow and said 'e wanted to be buried where it landed, and it landed under this bloody big tree, so they planted 'im there. And he was a Saxin English nobbleman really, not just a robbin bugger an' he couldn't shoot an arrow all the way out of England, could he? So he must 'ave been buried in England an' I know for sure 'e was buried in Sherwood Forest under this big oak tree an' I know for sure that 'e was done in by the Sheriff of Nottingham, so it goes to show that Nottinam's in England, doesn't it?'

Georgie's reasoning was impeccable. Even Billy was impressed. Having established himself as an authority on Robin Hood, he continued to relate the story of the outlaw and his Merry Men that he had just read in a borrowed copy of the *Rover* comic, Bumper Edition.

Robin Hood had long been one of our heroes, but we had never heard his full biography until now. His idea of robbing the rich had always attracted us, even though we had never actually encountered anyone rich. The idea of then giving the proceeds away however, was less attractive, irrespective of how poor the recipients might be.

What we had not realised before, was that the Merry Men had complete control of Sherwood Forest. Nobody, according to Georgie's account, was allowed in the forest without the express permission of Robin Hood and his band of outlaws.

'Are you sure about that?' I pressed Georgie on this particular point. 'Nobody was allowed in without askin' Robin?' Using the outlaw's first name seemed the natural thing to do; I felt so much of an affinity with him. 'If nobody was allowed in, how come some bugger done him in?'

Georgie's brow furrowed. 'Shot 'im when 'e was in Nottinam, in England,' he replied, after several seconds of deep thought. Certain inconsistencies seemed to be creeping into Georgie's account.

'If 'e was shot in Nottinam, how come 'e managed to shoot an arrow to gerrimself planted in Sherwood Forest?' I asked.

Georgie blushed a bright pink, but quickly recovered. 'Christ Almighty, he went 'ome after 'e got shot, didn't 'e? I only said 'e was shot didn't I? I didn't say 'e was shot dead, did I? The Sheriff of Nottinam wasn't much good an' instead of 'is arrow piercing Robin's heart it only gorrim in the bollocks.'

Georgie's obvious knowledge of history, geography and anatomy convinced me.

Our discussions continued until it was nearly tea-time.

'I'm getting hungry!' Terry announced, jumping down from his seat on the wall. One by one we followed, agreeing to meet later in the backyard of No. 43.

'I've been thinkin' about what we was sayin' about Robin Hood. You know, about him not allowing anybody in Sherwood Forest.' I addressed Tommy, Billy, Georgie and Terry as they sat on the tiles with their backs to the kitchen wall. ''Ow big is Sherwood Forest?'

'Worra you mean, 'ow big is it? How the bloody 'ell should I know 'ow big it is?' Georgie answered, irritated at such trivia.

'Well seein' as you're such a bloody expert at geography and suchlike, I thought you was bound to know,' I retorted.

Georgie's pride was stung. 'Well I know it's bloody big, 'cause it's got a bloody big oak tree growing in it!'

'Well is it as big as Sevvy Park?' I persisted.

Georgie spoke slowly, as though he was addressing the sub-normal. 'Of course it's bigger than Sevvy. Stands to reason, I thought anyone would know that.' Georgie's logic was again impeccable.

'How many outlaws did Robin have?' I broached another issue.

Having reasserted his position as expert in such matters, Georgie answered without hesitation. 'Five,' he stated, emphatically.

Five, five outlaws; the same number as us, and he exercised complete authority over Sherwood Forest. Sherwood Forest, a tract of land much bigger than Sefton Park.

That settled it.

'Right then, I votes we become outlaws and go and live in Sevvy Park and keep every other bugger out of it!' I knew that would touch a nerve with them. As we said before, we were all fed up with the crowds. Sevvy would be a much better place without them.

'Just imagine that,' said Tommy, 'just imagine Sevvy all to ourselves.'

'We could do what the 'ell we liked!' Terry enthused. 'We could run the café an' 'ave all the ice cream to ourselves, and we could clear out all the park keepers and bash their sodden 'eads in if they tried to get back in. I don't mind doin' that, Spud.'

Billy cheered. 'Bloody good idea that, Spud. We can put up notices warning them, an' if they keep coming we can shoot the buggers!'

Georgie, the logician, wasn't convinced. 'What are we gunner shoot them with, and what about the grown-ups? We 'aven't got nothing to shoot them with.'

'We've got our bows and arrows, just like Robin Hood.' It was my turn to introduce a bit of logic.

'I 'aven't gorra bow,' Tommy reminded me.

I couldn't believe what I was hearing. 'Well make a bloody bow then! Christ Almighty, do I 'ave to tell you everything. You can get a bit of string can't you, and you can get a stick can't you, an' you can make a sodden bow from 'em. Christ Almighty...' Further words failed me. It was so difficult being their leader, at times.

Terry had been quietly turning the idea over in his mind. 'No problem with the bows; in any case they'll prob'ly all go when we've warned them, so we won't 'ave to kill 'em. It's just that ... well if we go and live there, you know what'll 'appen. She'll only start moanin', she'll only come an' get me.'

Terry had a point. Our various mothers did have this habit of interfering with our plans.

'Ok then, we don't exactly have to live in the park, we just go there every day and see off anybody who hasn't read the notices. We just go an' tell them to sod off, then come back home.' This seemed to me to be a reasonable compromise.

'Trouble is,' Terry continued, 'if me mam finds out I've done some bugger in, she'll batter me.'

Now he had raised the issue, I suspected my mother wouldn't be too pleased with the idea of having a mass killer in the family, however good the cause.

'Ok then, we'll 'ave to make sure no one knows it's us. We'll 'ave to do it without anyone knowing it's us. We'll 'ave to do it incognitty.' I demolished another objection.

'What's an incognitty, I didn't think we were going to be incognitties. I thought we was gunner be like the Merry Men. I thought we was gunner be outlaws, 'cept we'd go home every night.' Tommy looked bitterly disappointed.

'Christ Almighty, don't you know nothing? Incognitty is bein' an outlaw.' It was my turn to talk down to the less knowledgeable. 'Incognitty means nobody knows it's you.'

'They'll know it's me alright,' retorted Tommy, still disappointed. 'Some bugger'll recognise me, they always do.'

I had to agree that he was probably right. How many times had we committed some minor infringement of our mothers' rules without a witness in sight, only to be faced days later with the dreaded instruction, 'Come 'ere you, I wanna 'ave a word with you about Mrs Taylor's kitchen window'?

I thought hard. Then it came to me. It was brilliantly simple. 'We'll wear masks!' I announced. They all cheered. Once again I had reminded them of why I was their leader.

'I don't mind wearin' a mask,' Billy agreed, 'but I'm buggered if I'm gunner be called a merry man!' he stated emphatically. It was hard to put your finger on why, but I had to admit that the title 'merry man' did not carry the ring of someone who engendered fear at first sight, someone who would shoot you without a second thought.

I thought fast. What was it we were going to do and how were we going to do it? Our name had to reflect our image. We were going to clear out everybody and do it in disguise and duff up anybody who tried to ignore our total domination of Sevvy Park. We would have masks to hide our identity as we avenged any transgression of our territory. What should we call ourselves? There must be a name that would portray the fear we would inspire.

That was it! I had it! A name that exactly described what we were about. A name that immediately conjured up the image of a desperate band of masked outlaws protecting their territory, fearless in all we do and fearsome to our enemies. And so on that day, a legend was born, the legend of the Masked Avengers.

The idea fired everyone's imagination. They were all so enthusiastic that I seriously considered asking for subscriptions, but memories were long as far as money was concerned. They would probably recall that earlier in the year I had started a savings club for fishing tackle at a penny a week. I only borrowed the first collection to buy a few sweets and fully intended to pay it back. Unfortunately, Billy's unannounced audit of the club's accounts had revealed the discrepancy. Punishment was swift and memorable, so I abandoned the idea of Masked Avenger membership subscriptions.

'I'm gunner get me mask, an' I'm gunner start shifting people out.' Billy stood up, fired with the idea of duffing someone up, particularly someone smaller than him.

He disappeared and returned a few minutes later wearing his winter hat: a woollen balaclava with one eye-hole bigger than the other and with a large unstable bobble on the top that flopped from side to side every time he moved his head.

It was not what immediately comes to mind, when you think of a mask, but that said, it certainly hid his face and he looked fearsome enough, if somewhat demented.

'Worrabout that, then!' Billy thrust his face at each of us in turn.

Nobody spoke; the effect was too disturbing.

'We'll 'ave to make ours,' I said faintly, having recovered from the shock of the first Masked Avenger. 'I'll see what I can find in the 'ouse.'

I dashed indoors and searched through all the cupboards. The best I could come up with was a cardboard box, used to keep some of the blankets in during the summer, and a small reel of elastic. A search of the coal shed produced a half-empty tin of green paint and a pair of rusty scissors.

'Tharrall you can find?' Terry studied the mask-making materials, taking the lid off the paint tin. 'No bugger's gunner be frightened of a green mask are they? Stands to reason, if you're gunner frighten 'em away, you've gorra have red, like blood. In any case we need bigger pieces of cardboard to make the notices.'

He was right. I went back in the house for another look. There was one place that I had so far avoided searching: Charlie's wardrobe. Ever since I'd borrowed his pyjamas for a Guy Fawkes and they had ended up as a pile of ashes, I kept well away from his wardrobe, particularly as Charlie had threatened a slow and painful transfer to the afterlife if I ever went near it again. The situation, however, demanded drastic measures, so I opened the wardrobe door.

Amongst Charlie's many heroes, was the Liverpool football team. Every Saturday night Charlie went through the back pages of the *Echo*, carefully cutting out pictures of his heroes and sticking them on large pieces of cardboard. Each collage of photographs was annotated in thick red pencil with the players' names. He had done it for years and there was the fruit of his labours, stacked at the back of his wardrobe, with his red pencil tied to one of the cards. They were perfect mask and notice making materials.

I was sure Charlie didn't like the crowds of people in Sefton Park any more than I did, so surely he would not object to me borrowing a few of his cards. In fact he would probably be grateful to have played a small part in the eviction of the troublesome hordes. I untied the red pencil and grabbed six of his cards from the back of the stack.

'That's more like it!' Billy carefully spread the cards out on the tiles. 'Cor, look at these pictures.' He began to tear off the photos and stuff them into his pocket.

Certain doubts about Charlie's support for the Masked Avengers began to form in my mind as I watched Billy undo years of work on his treasured football albums.

'Worrare you doin'? Sodden 'ell, Charlie'll bloody marmalise you. You didn' 'ave to take his pictures off! I only borrowed cards so we could use the other side for our notices. Christ Almighty 'e'll bloody-well kill you when he finds out!' It wasn't the violent eradication of Billy that bothered me so much as the suspicion that he might advise Charlie how he came by the photographs in the first place, in an attempt to halve any trouble with Charlie, by sharing it with me.

'Oh shurrup! Don't know what you're worried about. If he tries anything, I'll shoot the bugger. Nobody will know who's shot 'im will they, 'cause I'll be wearing me mask.' Billy continued to remove the photographs.

The thought that Charlie might get shot overcame any further objection. If Billy shot him, the Masked Avengers could have the rest of his cards, and I could have his bike. The trouble was that Charlie might appear before we had made our disguise.

'I votes we go to Tommy's yard so nobody will bother us,' I suggested.

We knew Tommy could do more or less anything he wanted. Tommy's mother had a sort of abstract concept of parenthood. Her philosophy boiled down to giving Tommy complete freedom to do whatever he wanted, providing he was available to mind his little brother Montgomery when she wanted to go to the pub, and provided that whenever he was caught doing something wrong, he gave someone else's name.

If, during one of his rare appearances, Tommy's dad tried a bit of parentship, Mrs Green would tell her husband to 'Buggeroff an' leave him alone! Mind your own sodden business,' partly out of resentment at him interfering with her philosophy of sweeping problems under the carpet, but mainly because she wasn't absolutely sure that Tommy and his dad were related, except by marriage.

We gathered up the cards, and other bits and pieces, and went to Tommy's. The backyard door wasn't locked, but try as we might, we couldn't push it open far enough to get in.

'Somethin's in the way, I'll 'ave to climb over the wall. Giz a bunk up.' Billy jumped up and grabbed the top of the wall. Georgie bent down, clasped his hands together under his brother's foot, and heaved. Billy scrambled up, and sat astride the top of the wall. 'Sodden 'ell, no wonder the door wont open. Worrave you got all this bloody rubbish for?' Billy jumped down into the yard.

After a few minutes of Billy cursing and grunting, the door swung open. A rusting mangle lay on its side amongst mounds of sodden rags and newspapers. Montgomery's pram stood by the kitchen door alongside the family tin bath, both half full of water. Piles of bricks and wood from the debbie, and heaps of coal bore testament to Tommy's mother's idea of good housekeeping: 'Purrit in the yard, I'll tidy it up tomorrow.'

Billy rearranged the rubbish to give us enough space to sit down in a circle, with the mask-making materials laid out on the ground in front of us.

'We'll make the masks first!' I grabbed the scissors.

'You 'ave to draw them out first, an' when you've drawn 'em, you cut 'em.' Georgie's logical approach to everything was getting a bit tiresome. However, he had a point.

I carefully drew the shapes of classic bandit-style masks on one of the cards, then laboriously cut them out, one for each of us, except Billy, who still wore his distorted balaclava.

The masks were a bit ragged around the edges, but they would serve their purpose. I pierced the edges with the tip of the scissors and tied on pieces of elastic, to hold them in place.

'Right then!' I announced. 'This is the mask as turns you into a Masked Avenger.' I struggled to find words suitable for this solemn occasion, as I handed over the first completed mask to Terry. 'This mask'll make you incognitty, so make sure you wear it before you start being a Masked Avenger and battering anyone; specially if you're gunner shoot the bugger.'

We watched in respectful silence as Terry carefully pulled the mask over his eyes.

Not to be outdone, Terry solemnly intoned, 'I am now a Masked Avenger an' I swear that I'll ... what the sodden-'ell ... what the 'ell's happened. I can't see a bloody thing. Christ I can't see nothin' ... sodden-'ell, you 'aven't cut the bloody eye-holes out! ... Bloody idiot ... I'm incognitty alright, an' so is every other bugger!' Terry snatched the mask off and threw it at me.

I thought quickly. Being pronounced an idiot was not conducive to maintaining the military-like discipline required by the Masked Avengers, if we were going to rid Sefton Park of the troublesome hordes.

'Who are you calling an idiot. I knows I 'aven't cut out the bloody eyes. Christ Almighty, I know that, don't I! I didn't do it 'cause I 'ave to know exac'ly where your eyes is before I cut 'em out, don't I. Thought that was obvious. I only know where your eyes are when you've purrit on. Christ, I thought that would be obvious. Now stop being thick and purrit on again and I'll mark your eyes out and then I'll cut them out.'

Terry was obviously not convinced, but said nothing and replaced his mask. I made an elaborate show of marking out the position of the eye-holes. 'Right you can take it off now. I've marked your eyes exactly, so I can cut 'em out now, can't I?'

Half an hour later we were sitting in a circle wearing our disguise.

'I can hardly see out of mine, you've made the eyes too far apart.' Tommy shifted his mask from side to side, exposing one eye at a time.

'Sod off!' I cut Tommy short. 'You must 'ave moved your head when I marked it. Just cut another 'ole in it and shurrup. We're gunner make the posters now, so we can warn people to keep out.'

A long debate followed as we tried to find suitable wording to expel the crowds from our territory.

'I know!' Billy exclaimed. 'It's not got to 'ave too many words, so they can read it quick and buggeroff before we gerrem.' We all agreed, mainly because we didn't know how to spell too many words.

'Well, go on, what should it say?' Tommy prompted Billy, knowing that Billy was the best qualified amongst us in matters concerning threats of violence.

Billy's brow was furrowed in deep concentration. 'Well, it 'as to say what we mean. It 'as to say exac'ly what we mean and what it is we're gunner do. It 'as to say...'

'Christ Almighty we know worrit as to say. We know that; we wanna know how to say it! Just gerron wiv it, just bloody tell us worrit should say!' Terry, exasperated, interrupted Billy's musing.

Billy ignored him. 'Well, we've gorra make sure it says what we mean.' Terry's groan failed to interrupt him. 'We 'ave to explain to them how important it is to buggeroff, so as they understand, so as they know we've got bows and arrers. What we 'ave to write on the notice is...' Billy paused for a few seconds. 'What we write is...' We waited with bated breath. 'Gerrout or you'll gerranarrer up your arse!' Billy concluded.

'Ok, that'll do. We can put our name on the top an' then we can say the message,' I settled the issue.

More than an hour and a half was occupied carefully crafting our notices: four of them in all, one for each of the main ways into Sefton Park. The final result was dramatic:

NOTISE OF the Masked Avengers

BY ORDER

SEVVY PARK BELONGS TO US

SO BUGGEROFF

SO GETOUT OR YOU'LL GET AN ARRER

UP YOUR BUM

In the end, I thought it best to give them two warnings, so we added the 'buggeroff' part to Billy's first proof.

Most of the other notices in the park had 'By Order' on them. The one on the gate into the Palm House said 'No dogs allowed. By Order', and it seemed to work, because there were never any dogs in there. We were not sure what it meant, but it worked, so we put it on ours.

Terry suggested substituting 'bum' for 'arse' partly because his mam was forever telling him off for using the expression, but mainly because we couldn't make our minds up about the number of 'r's in 'arse'.

There was plenty of space left on the card, so we added a drawing of a mask, by way of reminding people that we were incognito. Billy then insisted on adding a picture of a heart dripping with blood, with an arrow running through it, just to make sure they understood the dire consequences awaiting anyone ignoring the warning. Unfortunately, the heart was a bit difficult to make out because we had to draw it over our failed attempts to spell 'arse'.

We had just finished our preparations, when the backyard door burst open. It was Reggie Crane.

Reggie lived at the bottom of the street with his dad, an out of work Docker, and his older brother Ernie. Ernie was, probably, the first youth in Liverpool to be officially classified a Juvenile Delinquent and spent most of his time commuting between his house, the Junior Magistrate's Court and Borstal. As a consequence we never saw much of Ernie.

We never really saw much of Reggie either and he was regarded with some suspicion, not only because he was his brother's brother, but also for having a job.

Reggie worked every Saturday, and as many days as he could sag school, for Mr Truman, the mobile Greengrocer. Mr Truman sold his wares from a clapped-out lorry, to customers in the wealthy environs of Childwall and Woolton.

Reggie always seemed to have lots of money from his wages. Even so, he supplemented his earnings by selling faded fruit and veg to our mothers, their state of decay making them unfit for human consumption as far as his regular customers were concerned.

Yes, we were suspicious of Reggie and not a little jealous.

'I wanner join warreveritwas you was talking' about,' Reggie must have overheard part of our conversation. 'I wanner be a masked warreveritwas, an' I can pay warreveritis to join.'

Renewed thoughts of advanced subscriptions crossed my mind. I thought hard. 'Alright then, you can join, it's a shillin' a week and we do it on Saturdays, so you'll 'ave to give up workin'.'

It was a master stroke, a perfect response to Reggie's request. We would extract a shilling a week from him until he ran out of money. By that time we would be richer than he was and he would still be out of work, so he wouldn't be able to keep up the subscriptions and we could sack him. A brilliant piece of strategy, no wonder I was their leader.

Reggie's mouth dropped open. 'Shillin' a week! Give up me job! You're barmy, you are. Forgerrit, go an' boil your 'eads.' With that he slammed the backyard door and disappeared. My strategy had gone slightly astray, but at least he'd buggered off.

''E's mental 'e is. Fancy not wantin' to be a Masked Avenger; 'e's mental.' Terry spoke our thoughts.

'If 'e knows about the Masked Avengers, 'e can tell on us when we've done someone in. I told you, there's always someone as knows it's me,' Tommy said despondently, 'there's always someone.'

'Anyone as knows about the Masked Avengers who's norra Masked Avenger has 'ad it. He can only tell if 'e's allowed to.' We could sense the look of cold determination on Billy's face under his distorted balaclava. ''An 'e won't be allowed to.'

We cheered up. If Billy said he wouldn't be allowed to, the probability was that Billy would ensure he wouldn't be able to.

'Don't forget to wear your mask when you shoot 'im,' Georgie reminded his brother. 'I don't want me mam worryin' about your gerrin' caught.'

We each donned our mask and sat in a circle, with the posters spread out in the middle. It was a sobering experience. The masks gave us an air of mystery, whilst the posters told of our deadly purpose. We were ready for our mission.

I stood up. 'Right then, let's get goin' to Sevvy Park! We don't need our bows an' arrers, we'll just batter them this time if they don't take any notice of the notices.'

We walked in silence along the jigger to the top of the street and on to Lodge Lane, secure in our disguise, with the rolled up posters under our arms to keep them from prying eyes.

'Who the bloody 'ell do you think you are, Spud?' A gang of kids from Hanley Street barred our path. I was aghast. We had barely left the inauguration ceremony of our clandestine organisation, heavily disguised, and we had been recognised. Maybe they were guessing.

'That's where you're wrong, see!' I retorted. 'It's not me, so buggeroff.'

The Hanley Street gang were not put off. 'Course it's not you, and that's not that bloody idiot Terry what's-is-name, is it? An' I suppose 'e's not Georgie an' 'e's...' The speaker's sarcasm tailed off and his face drained of colour.

Billy thrust me aside and confronted our tormentors. The distorted balaclava with its lopsided bobble gave an air of manic intent to the murderous
stare from the odd eyeholes. Bravado flipped to panic and before Billy could
carry out the first act of homicide on behalf of the Masked Avengers, the gang
fled.

We continued our way along Lodgy, across Croxteth Road and down
past the Lodge House of Sefton Park to the biggest field in the park, known
to us as the 'Old Farm Field'.

The Avengers sprawled on the grass to debate the next course of action:
where exactly to put up our posters. We decided there were really only four
main roads into the park. One ran along the side of the Old Farm Field,
another was at the Aigburth Road end of the Boat Lake, a third at the Iron
Bridge leading to the Fairy Glen and the remaining one near the tiddler
ponds by Old Nick's Cave. An hour or so later the posters were in place.

We decided on a more or less central position, as our base for assas-
sinating anyone who ignored the warnings: a grassy lawn on the bank of a
pond overlooking the statue of Peter Pan.

Half an hour later we had not seen a single soul. It was something of an
anti-climax.

'Well that's what they are supposed to do, innit?' Georgie insisted, when
Billy moaned about the lack of action. 'That's why we purrem up, innit? So
they're workin', aren't they?'

The words were hardly out of his mouth, when two little girls skipped
down the path and started to dance around the statue. They stopped a few
seconds later to stroke the bronze animals at Peter Pan's feet: rabbits and
mice and frogs, polished a shiny yellow by generations of tiny fingers.

'Well I'll be buggered,' Georgie leapt to his feet. 'They've gorra nerve!'

The little girls had not spotted us.

Billy's eyes gleamed through the slits in his balaclava.

'Shurrup!' I commanded in a hoarse whisper. 'Wait'll I tell you.' We
needed a battle plan. It was no use being rash; after all, there were two of
them.

Having satisfied myself that there were in fact only two, and that
they were about half our size, I ordered the Avengers into action. 'Right
then, you wait 'ere with me 'an Tommy,' I instructed Georgie. 'And you
go round the lake and get behind them an' chase 'em towards us.' Billy
did as he was told, anxious to see some action. He crouched down and
headed back along the path to the café, to get around to the far side of
the lake.

The little girls were cooing with delight as they stroked the animals,
amazed at their own courage in touching creatures that frightened the

wits out of them in real life. One of them, the smaller of the two, climbed a few feet up the statue to get a better look at Peter Pan's face.

I waited anxiously for sight of Billy. 'Where the 'ell is 'e? 'E should 'ave been 'ere by now, the dozy sod,' I whispered. The little girls tired of their game and retraced their steps along the path, out of sight of the waiting Avengers. 'Bloody 'ell they're goin' to gerraway!' I scrambled to my feet. 'Where are you, Billy, for Christ's sake; they're gerrin away!' I yelled.

'Don't worry, I'll gerrem!' we heard Billy's reply from the other side of the lake. 'There they are! I'll gerrem!'

Silence fell for a couple of seconds, then, 'Oww-oww, that's me 'ead! Oww, I'm gunner tell me mam on you. I wasn't gunner do nothing, I was only playin...'

Billy appeared, propelled down the path towards the statue by a large woman rhythmically slapping his head with the back then the palm of her hand, the bobble on his balaclava flopping from side to side with each slap. The little girls followed, skipping in time with Billy's bobble.

'Coo, he's horrible, isn't he? There's somethin' wrong with 'im, isn't there Mam? Why is he wearing a big hat in the middle of summer, Mam? He's got one eye bigger than the other, hasn't he Mam?' the girls chattered as Billy staggered backwards under the onslaught, until he collided with Peter Pan and fell over. The little girls' mother hovered over him, annoyed that his head was out of reach.

Peter Pan

They stopped a few seconds later to stroke the bronze animals at Peter Pan's feet: rabbits and mice and frogs, polished a shiny yellow by generations of tiny fingers

'I wasn't doin' nothing, honest Missus, I was only goin' to 'ave a look at Peter what's 'is name, honest; an' I bumped into 'em by accident, honest.'

'He was trying to get hold of me, Mam,' the smallest of the girls said, helpfully.

'Oh, he was, was he?' She tried to bend down and grab Billy, but the bulk of her stomach stopped her just short of his throat and she only managed a hold on the bobble on his balaclava. Puffing with exertion, she hauled him upright.

Billy's continued attempts to protest his innocence were thwarted by the tourniquet effect of the balaclava under his chin. All he could manage was a strangled grunt.

'Told you there was something wrong with him, didn't I Mam? He can't even talk properly, he only grunts a bit. He's a bit simple, isn't he Mam?' The little girls switched their observations from Billy's appearance to the state of his mind, then consolidated their views. 'Can he only grunt because he's got odd eyes and he's simple, Mam?'

By this time, Billy was turning bright purple, his face visible through the eye holes now much elongated by the large woman's vertical pull on his balaclava.

'Look Mam, he's going a funny colour, Mam. Ohoo! Look! his eyes have gone the same size, so he should be talking properly now, Mam, shouldn't he?' The effect of the shape of Billy's eyes on his ability to talk didn't seem to be reversible. He could still only manage strangled grunts.

Now he was on his feet, the pressure on his larynx reduced sufficiently for him to continue protesting his innocence. 'I wasn't doin' nothin', honest, Missus. I was only goin' to 'ave a look at Peter what's 'is name, honest.'

'Don't ... tell ... fibs!' With Billy's head back within range, the girls' mother resumed her rhythmic pounding, this time alternating between ears.

'Don't ... go ... frighten ... ing ... little ... girls ... you ... stupid ... little ... boy!'

She transferred her hold to his shoulder. The balaclava returned to its original shape. 'Ohoo! Look! His eyes have gone back to being odd again Mam. You just watch, he'll start grunting again.'

The large woman stopped the rhythmic pulverising of his ears to take a closer look at his eyes. Billy seized his chance. He wrenched his shoulder free, and fled. Despite her size, the girls' mother was surprisingly quick on her feet and she managed a well-aimed kick at him before he got out of range.

A quarter of an hour or so later we had regrouped. Billy sat on the grass with his mask stuffed in his pocket, one hand tenderly stroking his ears, the other clutching his backside. 'Where was you lot, I nearly 'ad them, both of them? Where was you?'

'We were waitin' for you, you were supposed to chase 'em into us, and you didn't.'

'No I bloody didn't, an' I'll tell you why I bloody-well didn't. I didn't 'cause this old bag gorrold of me an' battered me 'ead in, an' you should 'ave told me she was there. An' she battered me ears in as well, an' she kicked me right up the arse: that's why I didn't!' Billy bent over to indicate where the kick had landed. It seemed a reasonable excuse, so I let the matter drop.

'You better put your mask on,' I advised him. 'Someone might recognise you.' Billy's reddened face and swollen ears disappeared under his stretched balaclava.

'Well that's got rid of one lot.' Tommy, ever optimistic, stood up. 'She might 'ave battered you a bit, Billy, but I bet she's gone home, an' I bet she'll never come back again, neither.'

Billy stopped rubbing his backside. 'I bet you're right an' all, Tommy, I bet I frightened 'em alright. There's no way they'll be coming back.'

I must say she didn't look very frightened to me, and the two little girls looked positively elated. However, looks can be deceiving.

'Right!' I announced, 'there's no more 'ere, so let's go and make sure there's nobody in the Fairy Glen.' We set off at a fast pace, chanting our fearsome battle cry, just invented by Terry and sung to the tune of 'We are the Ovaltinies'.

'We-are-the-Masked-Avengers, so-you-all-bugger-off! We'll-stick-anarrer-up-your-arse, so bugger-off-before-we-get-yer...'

The Fairy Glen was a secret little place with a tiny meandering stream running all the way down to the Boat Lake. It was a natural hollow full of flowering shrubs and exotic trees, framed at one end by an ornate blue painted cast-iron bridge carrying the park's perimeter road. We loved it in the Glen, even though we were not exactly welcome visitors.

There were two legal ways into our favourite place, each protected by a gate with a notice proclaiming 'Children not allowed unless accompanied by an adult. By Order.' We had a great respect for such notices, particularly those signed 'By Order', so we always entered the Glen via the shrubs under the cast iron bridge.

The Glen was deserted.

'The notice must be working,' Terry observed. 'They've all buggered off. Let's go down to the Boat Lake.'

We walked in file along the winding path to the end of the Glen. Georgie carefully closed the gate behind us. Our notice was pinned to a tree just along the main track leading to the perimeter road.

'Might as well see if it's still there,' Billy suggested. 'Just in case the wind's blown it off, or something.'

Georgie led the way at a fast run, with the rest of us following a few yards behind. Suddenly he skidded to a halt. The effect was dramatic. Billy ran full tilt into him. Tommy ran into Billy, I ran into Tommy and Terry piled into me. We all ended up in a heap in the middle of the track.

'What the 'ell d'you do that for!' Billy attempted to disentangle himself from the heap.

'Shurrup!' Georgie's voice was pitched high with excitement. 'Just look at them buggers!'

There, standing on the path studying our notice, was a small boy and a little curly-haired girl leaning on a battered doll's pram. We scrambled into the bushes at the side of the track before they spotted us.

'Lerrem read it, it will frighten the life out of them an' then they'll go home,' Tommy advised.

Fear strikes people in different ways. The boy looked fixedly into the distance, apparently struck dumb by the mortal danger he was in, whilst the girl indulged in a fit of giggles. Their terror must have disorientated them, for instead of bolting in panic for the safety of home, they set off down the path towards us, pushing the pram.

'We'll gerrem as they come past us,' Terry whispered, his voice hoarse with excitement.

''Ang on a minute,' Billy whispered, one hand nursing his bottom. 'Are you sure there's nobody with them?' The intruders continued down the path towards us. They were definitely by themselves.

'Right, make sure you've got your masks on properly.' There was purpose in Billy's instruction.

'Aw, lerrem go, they're only little kids,' Georgie whispered, with a hint of nervousness in his voice. 'Let's wait an' get someone a bit bigger.'

Leaving them alone would mean totally abrogating the ideals of the Masked Avengers. The idea of waiting for someone bigger didn't appeal much, either. It wasn't a question of the bigger the better, so much as the bigger they were the more likely they were to retaliate.

No, they had to be forcibly ejected from the park.

With the intruders now only yards away from us, Terry had no doubts. Overcome with excitement and with fire in his eyes, he leapt to his feet screaming, 'Revenge of the Masked Avengers!' and fell upon the intruders with the rest of us close behind.

They completely ignored us, even when we grabbed them. The little girl chattered to her bedraggled doll in the pram whilst the boy stared fixedly ahead. Our screamed threats subsided to bemused silence. Where were their screams of terror and pleas for mercy?

The boy continued to stare into the distance as Billy got hold of his jacket and pulled him face to face. Then, as a sort of afterthought, he looked Billy up and down as though he had only just realised he was there. Apparently dissatisfied with what he saw, he kicked Billy in the groin and butted him on the nose, before transferring his gaze back to the far distance.

'Ohoo, oww, he bloody kicked me 'e did; an' 'e butted me sodden 'ead in!' Billy let go of the boy, clutching his groin with one hand and rubbing his nose with the other. The little boy took the opportunity to deliver another kick as Billy turned to us. 'Oww-oww-oww, 'e's kicked me arse in now! Christ sake, someone gerrold of 'im will you!' Billy clutched his backside and held his groin, his face distorted with a mixture of frustrated fury and agony.

Terry and Georgie each grabbed an arm, trying to wrestle the little boy to the ground. The boy reluctantly diverted his gaze to his captors, looked them up and down, then kicked them both in the shins, before returning to his study of the distant fields.

Terry and Georgie held on and finally managed to wrestle their captor to the ground. Tommy joined them, sitting on his stomach to prevent any further assaults upon their persons. The boy transferred his gaze to the heavens.

'We've gorrim now!' Georgie cried. 'We've got the bugger. What are we gunner do with him now?'

'We're gunner kill the sod, that's what!' Billy hovered over the prostrate form, still clutching his backside with one hand, with the other thrust down the front of his trousers to sooth his throbbing groin. 'And don't you sodden-well try to escape or I'll...'

The threat was lost on our captor. He settled contentedly on his back, staring up at the sky. The little girl continued to ignore the whole thing, busying herself with smoothing the doll's bedclothes.

'We'll chuck 'im in the river an' then we'll chuck her in as well. We'll kill the buggers by drownin' them in the river, that'll teach 'em a lesson!' Terry started to drag the boy towards the stream.

It was not the time or the place to argue with Terry's rationale, but I wasn't too sure that there was any point in teaching dead people a lesson.

However illogical it was, the boy seemed oblivious to his fate, never taking his eyes off the tops of the trees as he was dragged across the path, his heels carving parallel grooves in the gravel.

The girl finished tidying the pram, whispered something to her doll, then turned to us. 'If you don't lerrim go, I'll tell 'is big brother and you've 'ad it.' The curly-haired girl picked up the doll, cradled it in her arms and whispered in its ear. 'They've 'ad it then, 'aven't they luv? Your mummy knows what'll happen to them when I tell his big brother, doesn't she precious? He'll batter their bloody heads off, won't he dear?'

The Masked Avengers do not bandy words with girls: her threats meant nothing to us, so we ignored her. Our hasty search of the surroundings for any sign of big brothers was for no other reason than to subject him to the same fate, if he happened to show up.

There was nobody in sight, so Billy took over from Terry and started to haul the small boy to the stream. I was sure that this time our victim would descend into a paroxysm of fear, but all he did was to continue to stare fixedly up at the heavens.

The nearer our captor got to his last moments, the more I began to doubt the wisdom of despatching him and his girlfriend in broad daylight in Sefton Park. Mass homicide seemed just a little severe on such a lovely sunny day.

I ran over to Billy just as he reached the short slope into the water. 'I've got a better idea! Why don't we throw 'em into some nettles! That'll teach them an' it won't kill 'em if we drag them out again; an' they'll be able to tell everyone what happens if you go into Sevvy, an' so nobody else will come.'

Billy let go of his victim, giving the boy the chance to settle more comfortably on his back and continue his investigation of the firmament. Billy didn't argue about the change in strategy. He too was having some doubts about his future as Liverpool's first serial killer.

'Right, Tommy, go an' find some nettles!' I instructed. Tommy started to search amongst the bushes. 'Not there, Christ there won't be any there will there? Go an' look under the bridge!' I redirected Tommy's search. Liverpool was proud of its parks in those days, and nettles were definitely not allowed amongst its carefully nurtured shrubberies.

Tommy clambered down the bank, stepped into the stream, then disappeared under the bridge. He was back a few minutes later, breathless with exertion and excitement. 'There's tons of 'em under there!' he announced, proudly confirming the success of his mission by exposing a row of angry lumps on his wrists.

'If he doesn't lerrim go, his brother'll kill him, he will, won't he precious?' The curly-haired girl resumed the whispered conversation with her doll. 'He'll knock seven kinds of shit out of him, won't he precious? He will, won't he? Now let your mummy see if you need changin'.' She turned the doll upside down and studied its knickers.

'Shurrup you, you're gunner be chucked in an' all.' Terry wagged his finger at the girl. 'You shurrup or you're gunner be done first. Stop talkin' to that sodden doll!'

The girl ignored him. 'Mummy's just telling them what's going to 'appen to them, isn't she precious? And who's been a good little girl, not wettin' herself?'

Their complete lack of understanding of the agonising punishment about to be metered out to them was beginning to irritate The Avengers.

'For Christ sake shurrup will you! Stop talkin' to that rotten doll. Christ sake don't you know what's gunner happen. Shurrup will you!' Terry was beside himself with frustration. Instead of being panic-stricken and pleading for mercy, she kept talking to a doll.

'You'll have to close your eyes, precious, you'll have to keep them tight shut so you don't see what his big brother does to them when he knocks seven kinds of shit out of them. Promise Mummy you won't look.'

'Aw, shurrup,' Terry muttered, lamely. 'Chuck 'im in the bloody nettles Billy, I'm sick of listening to 'er talkin' to that sodden doll.' Billy hauled his victim down the slope, dragging him along the bank of the stream and under the bridge. The little girl followed, cradling her doll.

Our victim slid along on his back never uttering a sound, his eyes still fixed on the sky above, not even blinking when his head bumped over humps and tussocks of grass. Eventually we came to what looked like a large clump of nettles.

'That's them!' Tommy announced. 'Them's the nettles!'

'You sure they're nettles?' Georgie looked doubtfully at the tangle of weeds.

'Course I'm sure,' Tommy retorted, 'warrelse are they supposed to be? 'Ow the 'ell do you think I got these? Hey, look, they've changed colour.' He displayed the row of white blisters.

'Come 'ere you.' Billy turned to the girl. 'Stick your 'ands in them.' He pointed to the weeds.

'Go and boil your 'ead,' she retorted, and then addressed her doll. 'He can go and boil his 'ead, can't he precious, you'll like that, won't you luv?'

Billy was totally nonplussed at her flat refusal and turned to Georgie. 'You stick your 'ands in then.'

Georgie had been stung by nettles before, and it hurt; but he realised a refusal would mean a thump from Billy, followed by a visit to the nettles. He thrust his left hand into the weeds.

'Christ Almighty!' He gasped as the blisters grew like magic on his hand. 'Sodden 'ell, look arrem!' He sucked vigorously on the blisters, with a vague idea that he might be able to suck out the poison.

'Let's have a look.' The little girl had never seen the effects of stinging

193

nettles before. Georgie displayed his hand with a proud flourish. 'Law, you aren't half brave, you are,' she said. 'Will it kill you?' she continued, with increased interest.

The colour drained from Georgie's face.

'He isn't half brave, he is, precious. Look at all them poison spots.' She thrust the doll's face into Georgie's hand. 'Promise mummy you won't look when he drops dead.' She covered the doll's eyes.

'She's talkin' to 'er bloody doll again. I'm sick of 'er talkin' to 'er sodden doll. Chuck 'er in the bloody nettles, for Christ sake!' Terry was shaking his clenched fists in frustration. 'Chuck 'im in, then chuck 'er in, an' chuck that bloody doll in as well!'

Tommy and Georgie were studying each other's hands, their faces white with fear as they searched for signs of the poison spreading to their vital organs.

'It won't do you no harm. I've had it hundreds of times,' I reassured them. 'And I 'aven't dropped dead, 'ave I? They'll go away in a minute, so stop moaning.' I turned to our victim, who was till staring unblinking at the tree-tops. 'Right you, you read the notice an' you ignored what it told you; and the Masked Avengers got you, so you should 'ave took notice of what the notice said, and now...'

'He can't read yet.' The curly haired girl interrupted my proclamation.

'Shurrup you.' I continued my summing up. 'You were told what would 'appen when you read the notice an' now...'

'I told you, he can't read yet.' The little girl kissed her doll. 'He can't read yet, can he precious, he's only just started in the Infants, hasn't he luv?'

I hesitated. 'Worra you mean, 'e can't read?' I had this uneasy feeling that it might not be natural justice, punishing somebody for taking no notice of the written word, when they couldn't read. The others looked on expectantly, perhaps waiting for me to bow to the girl's implied plea for mercy.

'Serves 'im right then, doesn't it!' I retorted, with devastating logic. 'Let's chuck 'im in!' I returned to my summary of the proceedings. 'You took no notice, so you're gunner get done.' The victim seemed to be studying the flight path of a seagull. 'If you manage to get out again an' don't drop dead in the nettles, just tell everybody that Sevvy belongs to the Masked Avengers, so they 'ave to keep out.' I concluded my address, acutely aware that the subject of our wrath was taking absolutely no notice of me.

'What's a sevvy and what's a masked what's-it? Your mummy wants to know what a sevvy is, doesn't she precious?'

'What d'you mean, what's a sevvy?' I turned to the girl in disbelief. 'What the 'ell are you talkin' about? This is Sevvy!'

Terry interrupted further discussion. He was dancing up and down,

194

shaking his fists. 'She's talkin' to 'er bloody doll again. Christ Almighty, I can't stand 'er no longer. She keeps on whisperin' to it. Why does she keep on talkin' to it? Sodden 'ell, I'm goin' 'ome if I 'ave to listen to 'er anymore!' He sat down, exhausted.

I was becoming exasperated beyond measure by the victim's complete lack of any emotion. Bending down, I took hold of the boy's feet. 'Gerrold of 'is 'ands and we'll throw 'im in,' I instructed Billy. 'He'll soon forget about the sodden sky, then!'

We lifted him up still intently gazing skyward, and swung him to and fro. Then, with a shout of, 'the Masked Avengers forever!' we let go. He landed with a satisfying 'thump' in the middle of the nettles. We cheered and clustered around him waiting for the screams of agony as the nettles metered out his punishment.

He lay there, silently surveying the sky.

We crowded forward to get a better look at his wounds, but there was not a blister in sight. Billy approached nearer and tried to poke our victim to make sure he was still alive. His hand brushed the nettles. A rash of blisters erupted all over his hand.

'Oww ooh oww, sodden-'ell!' Billy sucked frantically on his hand.

'Them nettles will probably kill him and all, won't they precious, as well as the other two. And his brother will kill the rest of them when he gets here, won't he? Promise Mummy you won't look when all of them drop dead?' The little girl again covered her doll's eyes.

'Oh, norragain! ... she's...' Terry's anguish got no further.

He must have been the promised little boy's big brother. Whoever he was, he appeared from nowhere, but he seemed to know where he was going. A burly youth, at least a foot taller than us, crashed through the bushes, grabbed Billy, and started pummelling him about the head, pausing briefly to knee him in the groin.

The curly haired girl resumed her dialogue with her doll. 'Didn't mummy tell you he was coming and didn't mummy tell you he'd kill them? Now don't you look, like you promised.'

Our victim continued to ignore the proceedings. He was too engrossed watching a blackbird perched high in the trees above him.

Turning his attention to the rest of us, the big brother let go of Billy and picked up half a tree trunk; but his attention to Billy was all we needed. Billy's cries for mercy could be heard in the distance as we crossed the Old Farm Field, running like the wind.

We collapsed out of breath behind the safety of a rubbish tip used by the park's gardeners. After a few minutes we spotted Billy, minus his balaclava, running as fast as his bruised legs would carry him.

195

When he came within earshot, Terry called him. 'Over 'ere, Billy!'

Billy changed direction in full flight, stumbled and pitched head-long into the rubbish tip. He landed on the freshest part, just where the gardeners had dumped a great mound of nettles.

Billy lay perfectly still and quiet, face down in the nettles.

The pounding of his head by the little girls' mother at the Peter Pan statue and her kick to his backside, followed by the little boy's headbutt and knee in the groin, his first encounter with stinging nettles, and the second pounding of his head by the big brother, had left Billy numb to any further pain. He slowly struggled to his feet, his face and hands a mass of overlapping white blisters.

'Mine are going away a bit.' Tommy stretched out his hand to show Billy that his stings had lost some of their anger. 'I'll be alright now, mine won't kill me, but yours are spreading like mad. Cor, look at 'em.' Tommy studied Billy's growing array of blisters, the latest ones fighting for space amongst the others.

'You should do something about them before they kill you,' Terry observed.

Billy said nothing. Death would be a welcome respite from the pains in his backside and groin, his battered legs, blistered hands and face, and pulverised head.

'There's some stuff you can use to get rid of 'em,' Terry continued. 'I've forgotten warritis, but it cures you alright.'

Billy remained silent, thankful that Terry couldn't remember the means for taking him from death's welcome door to painful survival. Curing the nettle stings would do nothing for the rest of the pains racking his body.

Terry's brow furrowed in deep thought. 'I know!' he announced, triumphantly. 'They're called Duck Leaves. Duck Leaves, that's what'll cure them!' Now he'd said it, there was something that sorted out nettle stings, but Duck Leaves didn't sound right. For a start, ducks had feathers, not leaves.

I remembered a tip my mother gave me when a word didn't sound quite right. Substitute the other vowels one at a time for the first one in the word, and it might lead you to the correct word. 'Deck' was promising, but not right. I then tried an 'I'. No, Dick Leaves wasn't right either, though it did have a certain ring to it. Then I had it! 'Dock Leaves, that's what you want, Dock not bloody Duck Leaves! That's what cures them.'

'What's a Dock Leaf? Where d'you gerrem from?' Tommy demanded. 'I wouldn't mind some, just to make sure I don't drop dead.'

'They're all over the place,' I replied vaguely. 'Everywhere there's nettles, there's Duck, I mean Dock Leaves.' We began to search the edge of the rubbish dump, our task hindered by the fact that none of us had the slightest idea of what a Dock Leaf looked like.

Rather than admit ignorance of the native flora, we conducted a series of experiments on Billy's face using different leaves. Each application produced a confident, 'That's done it, look, they're gerrin better!'

Billy said nothing as the white blisters and the rest of his face gradually turned bright green under the administration of a variety of plant cures. Only once did he show some emotion: when Georgie innocently applied a large sprig of nettles.

A while later we decided to let nature take its course. Billy didn't seem bothered about meeting his maker and we had run out of new varieties of plants to try.

'Are we gunner wear our masks again? 'Cause mine needs fixing,' said Tommy, morosely, holding up the tattered remains of his disguise, damaged in the encounter with the intruders. Then he brightened up a bit. 'Well I suppose we don't 'ave to, we taught them a lesson, didn't we? I know we didn't kill 'em, but there's no doubt about it, they won't come back.'

Tommy seemed to be unaware that our victim had escaped our encounter with no ill effects whatsoever. In fact I wasn't even sure he knew he was a victim. Our assault appeared to have done nothing other than to assist him in his passion for studying the heavens, whilst lying on his back.

I stood up and removed my mask.

One by one, the others removed theirs.

'I've gone and lost mine, an' it's me winter's hat. Me mam'll kill me,' Billy said, quietly, and then a bit more enthusiastically, 'anyway, I'm going 'ome now, I'm fed up with being a Masked Avenger. It's tea time an' me mam said not to be late.'

'I'm fed up an' all, and I'm hungry.' Terry threw his mask on the rubbish heap. 'I'm going home before I get moaned at.'

Terry and Billy's reminder of our other responsibilities brought to an end the first punitive sortie of the Masked Avengers.

The Avengers regrouped the next day in the backyard of No. 43.

Billy's face was coated pink with a thick layer of calamine lotion. He occasionally thrust a hand down the front of his trousers to nurse their contents, then withdrew it to rub his backside.

Somewhat hesitantly at first, then with growing enthusiasm, we discussed yesterday's battles.

'Probably dead by now. Don't forget he probably didn't use Duck Leaves; and when 'e drops dead, his big brother will be frightened to go back, and 'e'll tell everyone and they won't come either, an' that girl and her sodden doll what she kept talkin' to won't come again.' In Terry's imagination, our expedition to rid Sevvy of the unwelcome hordes had been a complete success.

From now on we would have the park to ourselves. We all agreed, the job had been done and done well. Any stranger who happened along, who was unaware of our fearsome reputation, would be dealt with by our notices. So it was that we agreed to end the cult of the Masked Avengers and consign them to legend.

'What do I do with these, then?' Tommy produced his mask.

'Just keep it special,' I suggested, 'just in case.'

'Just in case of what?' Terry demanded. I ignored the question, just in case someone suggested we mount another expedition.

'I've gone and lost mine,' said Billy. 'An' me mam doesn't know yet,' he added with a tinge of concern. 'I'll 'ave to go back an' gerrit, but I'm going to keep these.' He produced the football photographs, stolen from Charlie, and spread them on the ground around him.

Billy had just finished admiring them when Charlie opened the kitchen door and stepped into the yard behind him. Charlie spotted the array of photographs. 'I didn't know you collected footy photos.' Charlie was amazed to discover that Billy was interested in something other than pain and suffering. 'I collect 'em as well.' Charlie knelt down to take a closer look, as Billy edged towards the backyard door.

'I've got that one there, an' I've got 'im as well, an' that one. An' I mark them as well, so as I know which match it was. I use a red pencil like you as well, an' I said that on mine. Blimey, my handwritin's just like yours. That just looks like my handwritin', that does. Sodden-'ell, that is my bloody handwritin'! Christ Almighty, these are my bloody photos!'

Billy jumped to his feet, snatched at the door latch and was halfway into the jigger when Charlie caught him with a kick to the backside. It got him on the same spot that the little girl's mother had found.

Epilogue

THE STORIES IN THIS BOOK were prompted by nostalgia: an attempt to ignore life's little problems by hiding behind memories. Living in wartime Liverpool 8 provided so many memories of a wonderful, carefree childhood that I thought I'd cracked it.

But what happened?

I tried to do a Tom Stoppard, but it turns out he got it wrong. I think Peter de Vries is a bit nearer the mark.

As I say, I tried to carry my childhood with me with the aid of the stories in this book. If things got a bit serious in my life, which they did as soon as I was forced to go to work, I sought solace by losing myself in childhood memories. But the older I got, the less time the memory lasted and the more real life insisted itself on me. At first I still had the Liverpool 8 of my childhood to help me hang on to the memories: when I went elsewhere to live, my mam stayed where my memories were formed and I visited her every week.

Even after the bulldozers arrived and Tagus Street disappeared, Mam stayed firmly put, close by: she still lived 'off Lodge Lane'. So at least whenever I visited my mam, the memories came alive. But then she passed away and my memories began to fade. De Vries, it seems, was right: nostalgia isn't what it used to be.

Certainly, Mr Stoppard had got it wrong; though I carried my childhood with me, my book of memories, it didn't stop me getting older. In fact I'm now quite ancient, older even than the Bible's allotted time. Neither, Mr Stoppard, can I still climb trees nor run away from Bobbies!

There are still signs of my childhood Liverpool. Magnificent buildings: the Three Graces dominating the waterfront; the Liver building, Cunard and the Port of Liverpool buildings; St George's Hall, the Art Gallery, the Libraries, and many, many more ignored or missed by the Luftwaffe. There are even bits of what look like bombed sites, but they are very few.

Liverpool City centre is now Liverpool One: the ultra modern shopping mecca (with its very own John Lewis store, a Harvey Nichols and Hotel Chocolat!) and of course the wonderful Albert Dock: a World Heritage Site and the home of museums, ferries across the Mersey and shrine to the Beatles!

Acknowledgements

IF I ATTEMPTED TO THANK all those who had helped get me to the point where I produced this work, I would need another book to record them, so I will confine these thanks to those who have directly contributed to its publication.

Having abandoned thoughts of publication some years after writing, it was Jimmy Sweeney, a fellow Scouser, who idly worked his way through a long-neglected draft and observed that 'this is not bad, I've seen a lot worse'. Not wanting to deprive the public of the chance to read something a bit better than what they are apparently used to, I sought interest beyond Jimmy's literary circle.

So you see if you don't like *Toxteth Tales*, blame Jimmy, not me!

More seriously, there are numbers of photographs in the work that are there because of the support and help of the staff nurturing the archives of Liverpool's Maritime Museum, specifically the Stewart Bale Collection. In particular I must thank Anne Gleave and Nathan Pendlebury.

My thanks also go Merseyside Police who responded instantly to a request to use their copyright photo 'WW2 Bomb Damage, Liverpool South' and to Colin Wilkinson, Bluecoat Press for his permission to use the picture of the Solway Arms, included to illustrate my Granddad's love of Walker's Warrington Ales

Some years ago, with the manuscript for the book a heap of handwritten sheets of paper, it was Vanessa, my Daughter, and Sylvia, my Wife, who translated the sheets into ubiquitous Microsoft 'Word' and gave them back to me in a form that I could endlessly play with.

Vanessa then produced more support for me in the form of my grand-children: Oliver and Sophie.

Now I must thank the person responsible for turning a computer file into the book you are holding. It was Anna Goddard of Carnegie Publishing who responded to my request for publishers to consider giving the public a chance to read this work.

Lastly but certainly not least I thank you, dear reader, for giving the book a try: I hope you liked it.